1 Counting at the beach

Look carefully at this picture. How many different things can you count?
Write the answers in the boxes.

seagulls	deckchairs	sandcastles	shells	buckets
1	2	3	10	5

2 Word scrambles

There are two words hidden in each row of scrambled letters.
The pictures are clues to the words. Write the words on the lines.

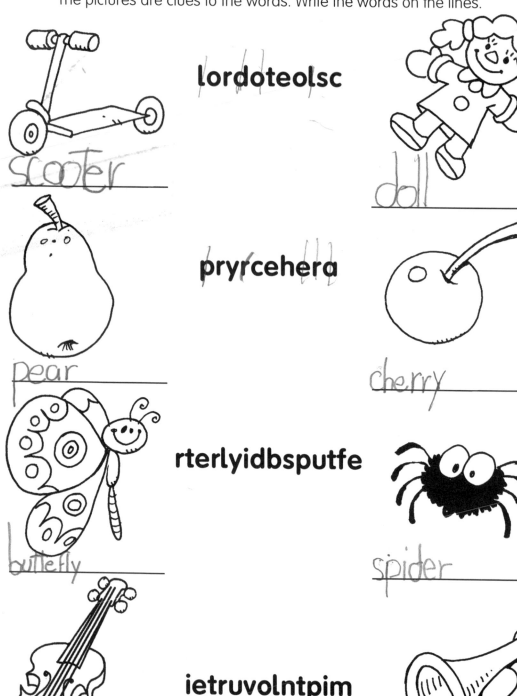

lordoteolsc

scooter

doll

pryrcehera

pear

cherry

rterlyidbsputfe

buttefly

spider

ietruvolntpim

vilon

3 Spooky spellings

Tick the correct spelling for each of the pictures.

☐ dragen
☑ dragon

☑ which
☐ witch

☑ whizard
☐ wizard

☐ gost
☑ ghost

☑ pumpkin
☐ pumkin

☑ castle
☐ cassle

4 Things that go wordsearch

Look in the wordsearch grid for seven types of transport.
You will find them by reading across or down.
Draw a ring around the words as you find them.

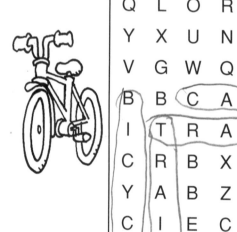

Q	L	O	R	R	Y	B	B	H
Y	X	U	N	L	P	C	U	E
V	G	W	Q	R	U	T	S	L
B	B	C	A	R	H	A	Q	I
I	T	R	A	C	T	O	R	C
C	R	B	X	A	Q	C	J	O
Y	A	B	Z	G	H	O	J	P
C	I	E	C	U	J	S	G	T
L	N	O	P	S	F	R	D	E
E	X	W	Q	Z	B	C	X	R

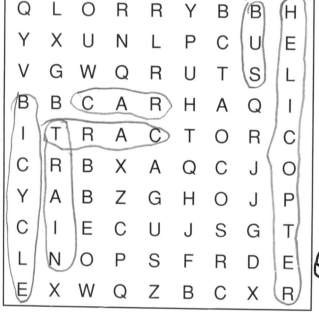

5 Going quackers

Help the ducks through the maze to their ducklings
by following the numbers in the five times table.

6 **Garden games**

Look carefully at these two pictures.
There are 10 differences. Can you spot them?

7 **On safari**

Unscramble the names of these safari animals.

8 Odd pigs

Count the pigs in the pig pens. Circle the pens that have
an ODD number of pigs.

⑨ Top gear

Look at the symbols in the box. Each symbol represents a different number of minutes. Add up the times to see which car finishes first.

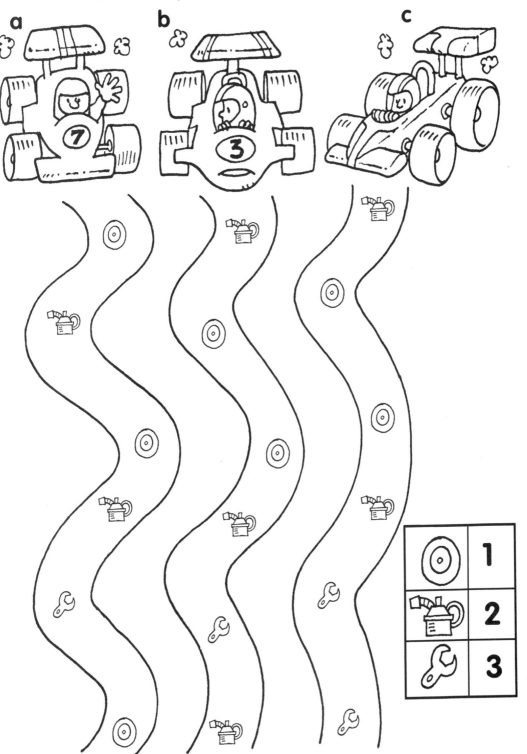

10 Missing middles

These words are missing their middle letters.
Complete the words using the pictures as clues.

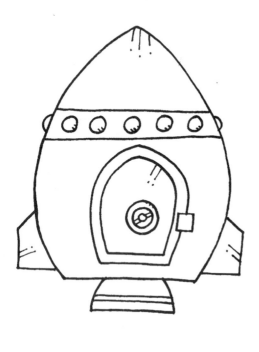

ro_ _et

ja_ _et

an_ _or

ba_ _et

11 **Odd one out**

Look at each row of objects.
Put a tick next to the picture that is the odd one out in each row.

12 Flying high

Follow the tangled strings to see which kite each child is flying.

13 Ladybird, ladybird

Draw lines to match the pairs of ladybirds that are the same.

14 Rocking around the pool

Help the crabs through the maze to the rock pool.

15 Animal magic crossword

The pictures of animals are clues to the words.
Follow the numbers across and down, and write the words in the grid.

16 Beginning with 's'

How many things can you see that begin with the letter 's'?

17 Number patterns

Look at the numbers in the balloons and write
in the missing numbers.

18 Prehistoric dot-to-dot

Starting with the letter 'a', draw a line to join the dots
and complete the picture.

19 Opposites

Draw lines to join the words that are opposites.

big

day

happy

slow

fast

small

night

sad

20 Picture wheel

Write the first letter of each picture in the space in the centre of the picture wheel. You will spell the name of a fruit.

21 Sums puzzles

Do the sums in the grids by filling in the missing numbers and symbols.

15	÷	3	=	
−	■		■	+
3	−	2	=	
=	■	=	■	=
	−	6	=	6

	−	16	=	3
+	■	−	■	+
2	+		=	14
=	■	=	■	=
21		4	=	

22 Weather scramble

Unscramble the letters to spell the words.
Write the correct spelling on the lines.

iwnbora

_____

ulrlabme

_____

itacoran

_____

tosob

_____

tah

_____

udocsl

_____

23 Addition

Do these addition sums.

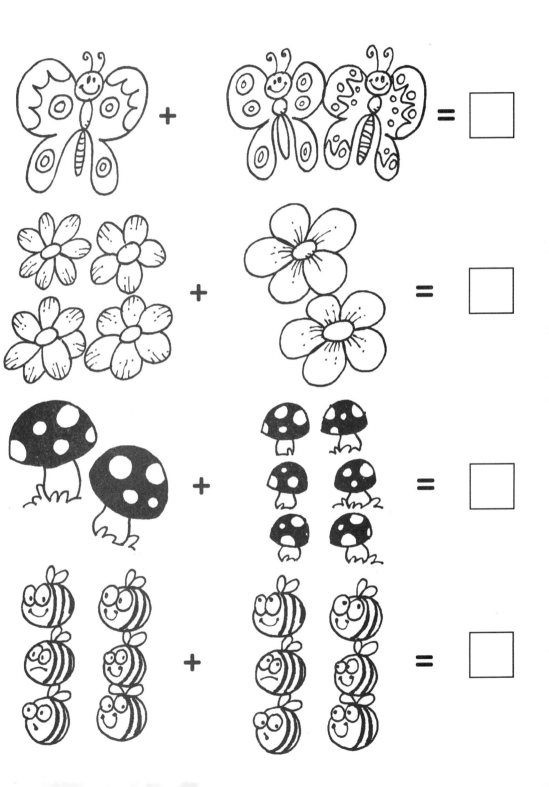

24 Weight for it!

Who is heavier?

Who is lighter?

Who is heavier?

Who is lighter?

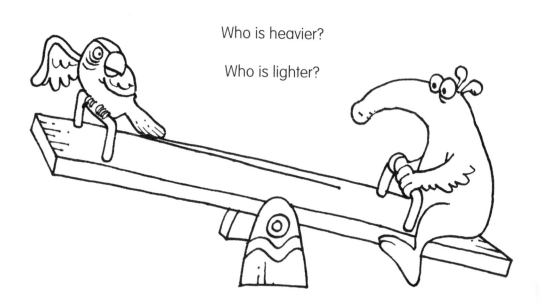

25 Size wise

How long is Sid the centipede?

How long is Molly the millipede?

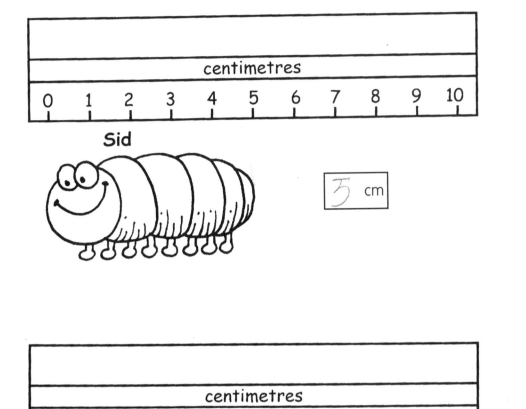

				centimetres					
0	1	2	3	4	5	6	7	8	9	10

Sid

5 cm

				centimetres					
0	1	2	3	4	5	6	7	8	9	10

Molly

9 cm

Who is longer?

Who is shorter?

26 **Make it plural**

Write the plural spellings for each of these words.

car

_____

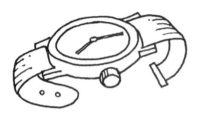

watch

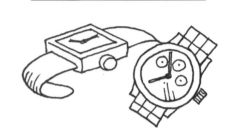

_____

apple

_____

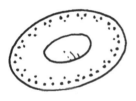

dish

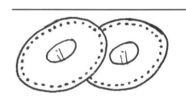

_____

tree

_____

27 Copy and draw

Copying square by square, use the grid to help you draw
the other half of this butterfly.

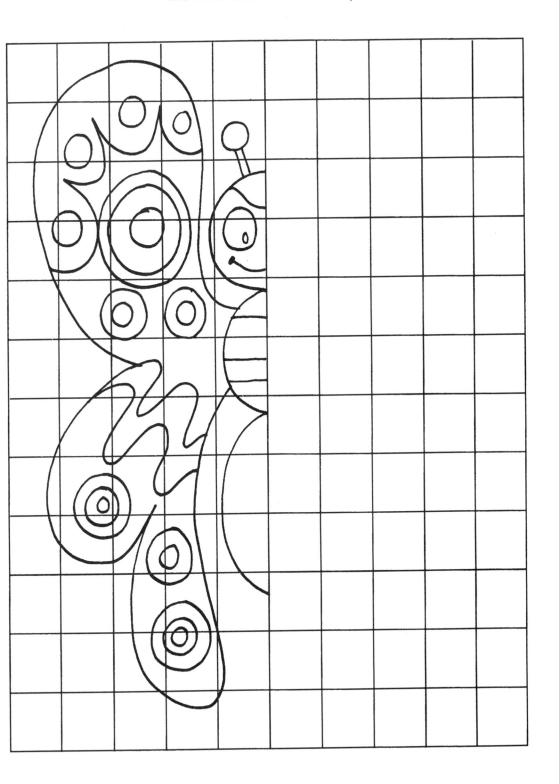

28 Funny farm

Look at the picture and find eight things that have gone wrong.

29 Penguin silhouettes

Draw lines to match the penguins with their silhouettes.

30 Heads and tails

Write the first letter of each picture in the boxes.
You will make a new word.

☐ o ☐

☐ a ☐

☐ a ☐

☐ i ☐

31 The most sheep

Count the number of sheep each farmer has.
Circle the farmer with the MOST sheep.

32 Trivia

Who invented television?
a. Terry Vision
b. John Logie Baird
c. Guglielmo Marconi

33 Trivia

In which country is the leaning tower of Pisa?
a. France
b. Germany
c. Italy

34 Adding 'e'

Add 'e' to these words to make new words.

us + e =

can + e =

car + e =

pin + e =

35 Letter codes

Using the code in the box as a guide, fill in the missing letters to spell an animal.

	1	2	3	4	5	6
A	b	k	g	o	p	w
B	d	c	e	r	a	m
C	r	h	f	l	q	c
D	f	p	x	d	i	o
E	g	y	f	k	u	w
F	e	z	c	f	a	b

g l r a f f e
A3 D5 C1 B5 C3 E3 F1

36 New words

How many new words can you make from the word 'dinosaur'?
Write the new words in the dinosaur's body.

dinosaur

37 Word trail

Use the picture clues to fill in the word trail. The last letter of each word is the first letter of the next word.

38 Hocus-pocus

Look at the pictures and work out the correct order of this story.
Write the numbers 1 to 4 in the boxes.

39 What is it?

Starting with the letter 's ', cross out every other letter to spell a word.
Write the word on the line.

sprelnmgoutizng

_____

40 Weather code

Use the code to work out the answers to the sums.

1	2	3	4	5	6

$$5 + 3 = 8$$

$$6 + 1 = 7$$

$$2 + 4 = 6$$

$$3 + 6 = 9$$

$$1 + 2 = 3$$

41 **Copy and draw**

Copying square by square, use the grid to help you draw this picture.

42 **Playtime problems**

Look at the picture and find eight things that have gone wrong.

43 Pirate silhouettes

Draw lines to match the pirates with their silhouettes.

44 Heads and tails

Write the first letter of each picture in the boxes.
You will make a new word.

45 The least presents

Count the number of presents each child has.
Circle the child with the LEAST presents.

46 What is it?

Starting with the letter 'x', cross out every other letter to spell a word.
Write the word on the line.

xlgandoypbwiqrads

_____

47 The hare and the tortoise

Look at the pictures and work out the correct order of this story.
Write the numbers 1 to 4 in the boxes.

48 Word trail

Use the picture clues to fill in the word trail. The last letter of each word is the first letter of the next word.

49 New words

How many new words can you make from the word 'scarecrow'?
Write the new words in the scarecrow's coat.

scarecrow

50 Letter codes

Using the code in the box as a guide, fill in the missing letters to spell something with wheels.

	1	2	3	4	5	6
A	a	q	w	c	d	r
B	t	y	u	i	o	e
C	p	h	b	g	s	z
D	i	c	v	b	y	n
E	m	e	f	o	t	l
F	e	n	p	c	i	b

‾‾ ‾‾ ‾‾ ‾‾ ‾‾ ‾‾ ‾‾
C3   D1   A4   D5   F4   E6   B6

51 Adding 'e'

Add 'e' to these words to make new words.

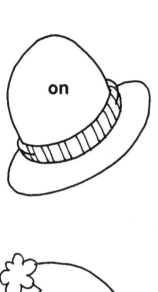 **on** + $\boxed{e}$ =  *one*

 **cap** + $\boxed{e}$ =  *cape*

 **pip** + $\boxed{e}$ = *pipe*

 **her** + $\boxed{e}$ = 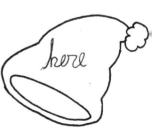 *here*

52 Trivia

Which is the correct spelling for a group
of cows?
a. a heard
b. a herd
c. a hird

53 Trivia

Which of these is another word for a 'ghost'?
a. a speckle
b. a spectre
c. a hector

54 Subtraction sums

Do these sums.

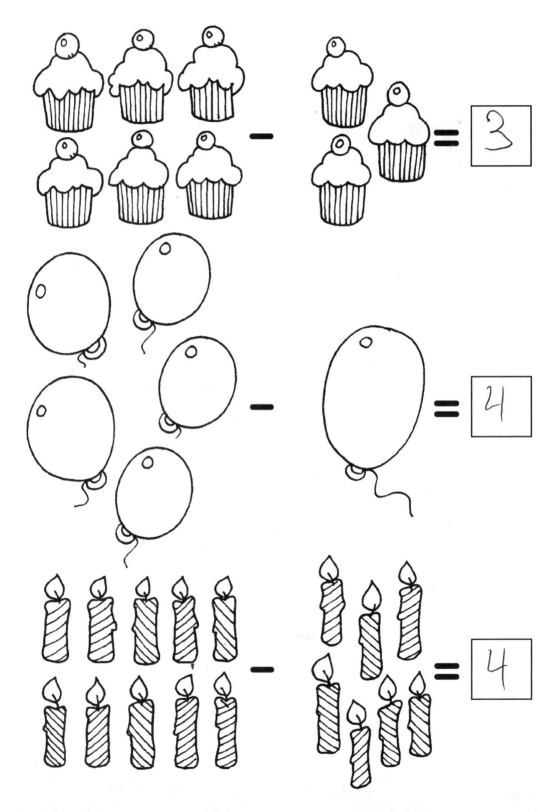

55 Hidden words

In each grid, cross out the letters that appear more than once to discover the hidden words. Write the words on the lines.

e	p	o	l	s
m	r	h	u	a
b	s	g	l	v
u	o	r	e	i
c	v	b	h	p

_____

t	e	r	h	m
c	q	w	z	z
q	m	b	c	a
n	h	d	e	t
b	o	r	o	z

_____

56 Garden code

Use the code to work out the answers to the sums.

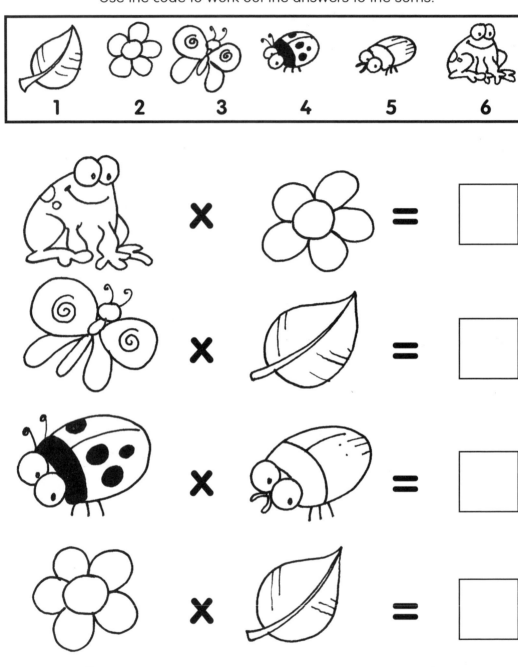

57 Missing hands

Draw the hands on the faces of these clocks.

9.15

one o'clock

half-past three

7.45

58 Dividing

Do these division sums and draw lines to match the answers
with the correct group below.

$$10 \div 2 = \boxed{}$$

$$12 \div 3 = \boxed{}$$

$$15 \div 5 = \boxed{}$$

$$18 \div 3 = \boxed{}$$

59 Counting by the pond

Look carefully at this picture. How many different things can you count?
Write the answers in the boxes.

dragonflies	fish	ducks	frogs	lily-pads

60 Word scrambles

There are two words hidden in each row of scrambled letters.
The pictures are clues to the words. Write the words on the lines.

 **ogritienl**

_____ _____

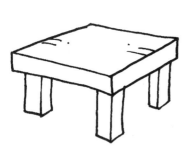 **hlaibaecrt**

_____ _____

 **onbiecklop**

_____ _____

 **rtsirsedks**

_____ _____

61 Animal spellings

Tick the correct spelling for each of the pictures.

☐ **giraffe**
☐ **gereraff**

☐ **kangeroo**
☐ **kangaroo**

☐ **koalla**
☐ **koala**

☐ **gorilla**
☐ **goriller**

☐ **tieger**
☐ **tiger**

☐ **zebra**
☐ **zeabra**

62 Under the sea wordsearch

Look in the wordsearch grid for seven things that live in the sea.
You will find them by reading across or down.
Draw a ring around the words as you find them.

```
O  C  T  O  P  U  S  J  T
X  K  J  B  S  Q  P  X  E
S  T  A  R  F  I  S  H  S
U  W  R  H  R  D  F  P  P
W  H  A  L  E  O  E  Q  Q
C  T  U  R  T  L  E  B  I
R  W  R  Q  V  P  H  X  D
A  Y  L  A  S  H  J  C  V
B  G  H  A  F  I  S  H  B
E  B  X  W  Q  N  Y  D  A
```

63 The fair's in town

Look carefully at these two pictures.
There are 10 differences. Can you spot them?

64 Walkabout
Unscramble the names of these cities.

ONLNDO

LUBIND

FRCDIFA

UBDEGINRH

65 Even cakes

Count the cakes on the trays. Circle the trays that have
an EVEN number of cakes.

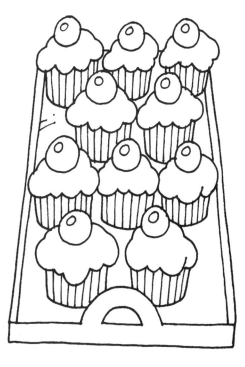

66 Pyramid problem

How many triangles can you count in this picture?

67 Flower power crossword

The pictures of flowers are clues to the words.
Follow the numbers across and down, and write the words in the grid.

68 Goal!

Help the boy to score a goal.

69 Skating fun

Draw lines to match the pairs of skates that are the same.

70 What a catch

Follow the tangled fishing lines to see which gnome caught the middle fish.

71 Odd one out

Look at each row of objects.
Put a tick next to the picture that is the odd one out in each row.

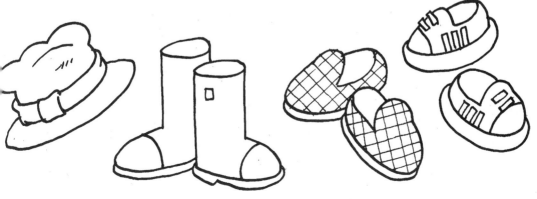

72 Missing middles

These words are missing their middle letters.
Complete the words using the pictures as clues.

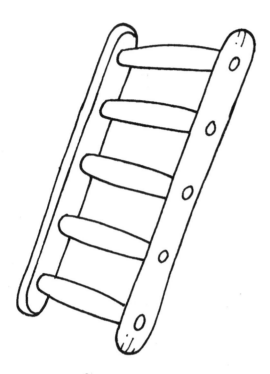

la_ _er

pa_ _ot

ra_ _it

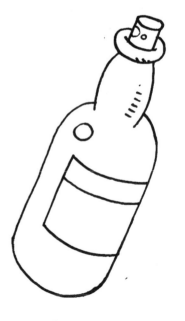

bo_ _le

73 Seaside code

Use the code to work out the answers to the sums.

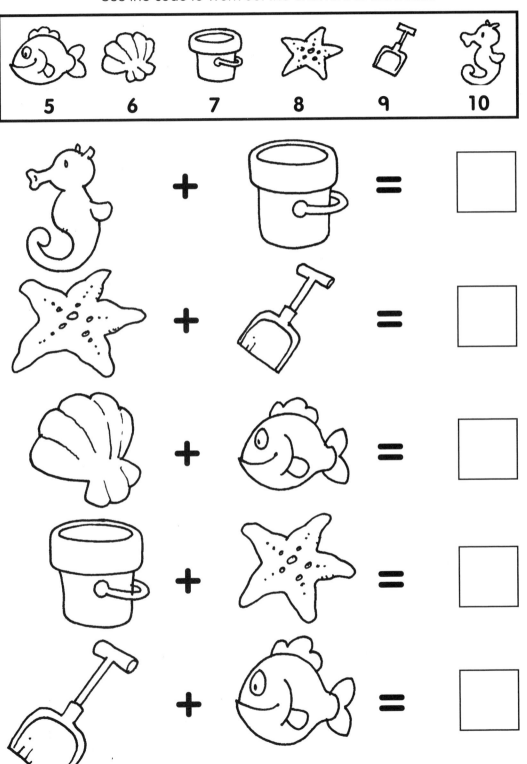

74 High flyer

Look at the symbols in the box. Each symbol represents a different number of minutes. Add up the times to see which bird is fastest.

75 Weigh it up

Draw some more apples on these scales so that they balance.

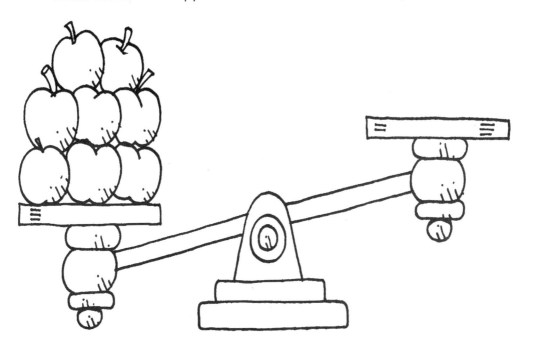

Draw some more bananas on these scales so that they balance.

Do these addition sums.

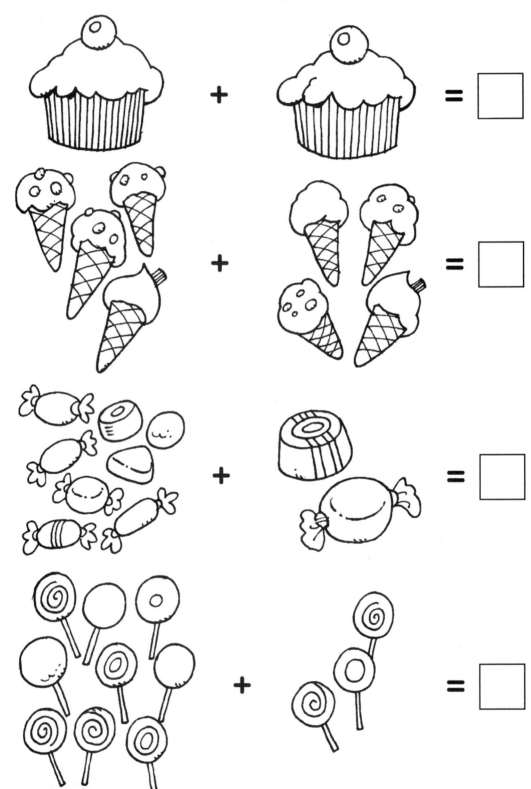

77 Mini-beast scramble

Unscramble the letters to spell the words.
Write the correct spelling on the lines.

tyuerlbtf	omwr	aydrldib
_____	_____	_____

elbete	tna	eiplactrlra
_____	_____	_____

78 Sums puzzles

Do the sums in the grids by filling in the missing numbers and symbols.

3	+		=	12
×	■	×	■	
	÷	2	=	6
=	■	=	■	=
36	÷		=	2

7	+	4	=	
	■	−	■	+
3	×		=	9
=	■	=	■	=
21	−	1	=	

79 Picture wheel

Write the first letter of each picture in the space in the centre of the picture wheel. You will spell the name of someone who makes things disappear!

80 Opposites

Draw lines to join the words that are opposites.

tall

up

light

hot

down

cold

heavy

short

81 **Windy days**

Starting with the letter 'a', draw a line to join the dots
and complete the picture.

82 Number patterns

Look at the numbers on the snakes and write
in the missing numbers.

83 Wiggly worms

How long is Wally?
How long is Wendy?

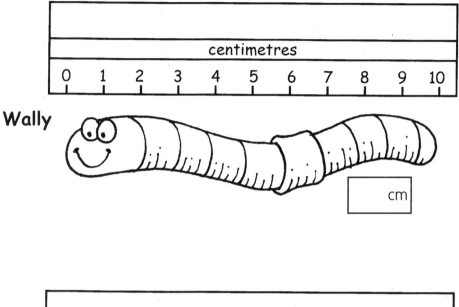

centimetres
0 1 2 3 4 5 6 7 8 9 10

Wally

cm

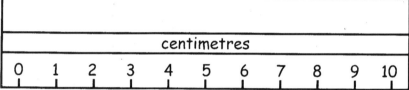

centimetres
0 1 2 3 4 5 6 7 8 9 10

Wendy

cm

Now draw your own worm that is six centimetres long.

centimetres
0 1 2 3 4 5 6 7 8 9 10

84 Make it plural

Write the plural spellings for each of these words.

fox

_____

boat

_____

sandwich

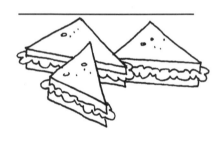

_____

glove

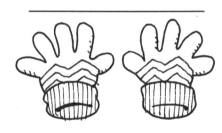

_____

brush

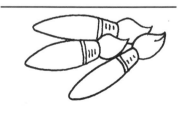

_____

85 Subtraction sums

Do these sums.

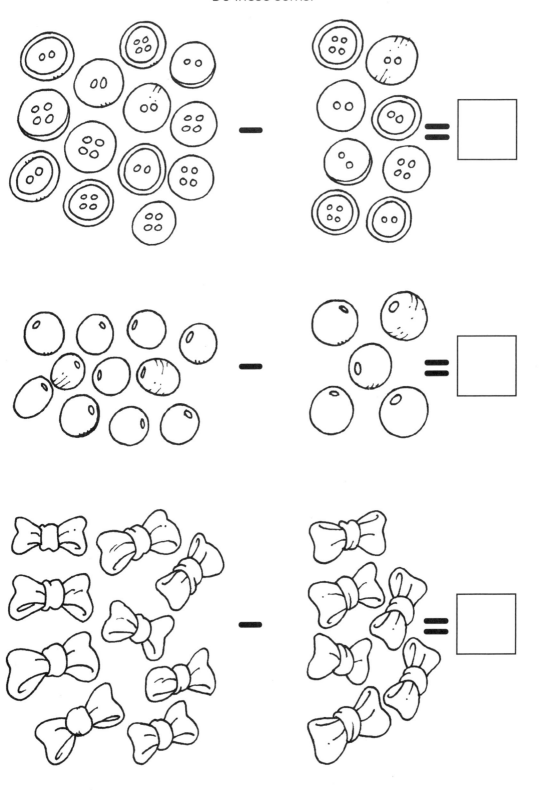

86 Copy and draw

Copying square by square, use the grid to help you draw the other half of this castle.

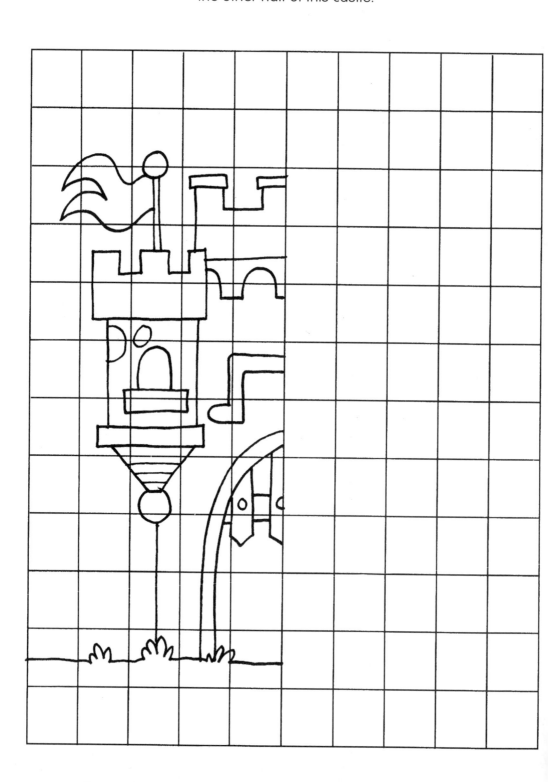

87 Football crazy

Look at the picture and find eight things that have gone wrong.

88 Children silhouettes

Draw lines to match the children with their silhouettes.

89 Heads and tails

Write the first letter of each picture in the boxes.
You will make a new word.

□ o o □

□ o o □

□ e a □

□ r i □

90 The most bones

Count the number of bones each dog has.
Circle the dog with the MOST bones.

91 Dinosaur sums

Count the spines on the dinosaurs and write the numbers on their bodies.
Then do the multiplication sums.

92 Trivia

What is a duck-billed platypus?
a. a mammal
b. a fish
c. a bird

93 Trivia

At what temperature does water freeze?
a. 100 °C
b. -10 °C
c. 0 °C

94 Adding a letter
Add a letter to these words to make new words.

car   +   t   =

cap   +   m   =

car   +   d   =

cow   +   r   =

95 Letter codes

Using the code in the box as a guide, fill in the missing letters
to spell an insect.

	1	2	3	4	5	6
A	m	l	k	n	h	b
B	g	t	f	t	d	e
C	u	z	a	p	o	i
D	w	e	b	t	y	r
E	a	l	c	f	b	n
F	i	s	u	p	t	y

D3   C1   B2   B4   B6   D6   E4   E2   F6

96 New words

How many new words can you make from the word 'sandcastle'?
Write the new words in the sandcastle.

sandcastle

97 Word trail

Use the picture clues to fill in the word trail. The last letter of each word is the first letter of the next word.

98 The snowman

Look at the pictures and work out the correct order of this story.
Write the numbers 1 to 4 in the boxes.

99 What is it?

Starting with the letter 'p ', cross out every other letter to spell a word.
Write the word on the line.

pwlipnrdgmhiblklz

_____

100 Hidden words

In each grid, cross out the letters that appear more than once to discover the hidden words. Write the words on the lines.

e	r	k	y	p
s	c	v	b	a
l	k	p	o	e
a	r	u	x	s
x	y	b	v	d

_____

i	n	s	p	g
t	b	z	u	h
w	p	h	c	o
g	r	u	n	i
z	c	m	b	w

_____

101 Missing hands

Draw the hands on the faces of these clocks.

3.30

quarter-to four

quarter-past six

11.15

102 Dividing

Do these division sums and draw lines to match the answers with the correct group below.

$$12 \div 1 = \boxed{}$$

$$24 \div 12 = \boxed{}$$

$$48 \div 6 = \boxed{}$$

$$49 \div 7 = \boxed{}$$

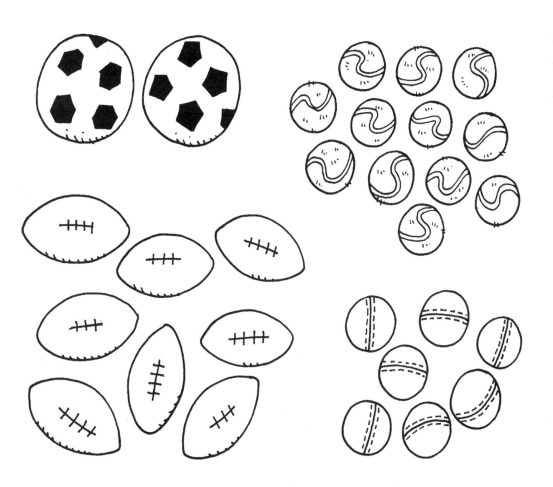

103 Counting on the farm

Look carefully at this picture. How many different things can you count?
Write the answers in the boxes.

tractors	scarecrows	cows	sheep	buckets

104 Word scrambles

There are two words hidden in each row of scrambled letters.
The pictures are clues to the words. Write the words on the lines.

 lwniloesarf

_____ _____

 eofrartarctmr

_____ _____

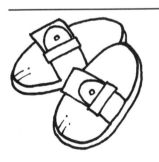 alsesdsanhos

_____ _____

 aizwndrdwa

_____ _____

105 Sea spellings

Tick the correct spelling for each of the pictures.

☐ **whale**
☐ **wale**

☐ **shels**
☐ **shells**

☐ **lobstar**
☐ **lobster**

☐ **dolfin**
☐ **dolphin**

☐ **krab**
☐ **crab**

☐ **fish**
☐ **fishe**

106 Girls' names wordsearch

Look in the wordsearch grid for the names of these eight girls.
You will find them by reading across or down.
Draw a ring around the words as you find them.

NICKY

SHARON

BECKY

GWEN

SARAH

```
W  M  D  F  S  U  B  B  X
S  A  R  A  H  G  P  E  O
V  R  F  O  A  B  N  C  U
N  I  Z  Y  R  R  C  K  W
X  A  J  T  O  V  A  Y  U
Q  F  C  G  N  A  N  C  G
J  B  T  G  W  E  N  O  X
L  O  R  N  A  H  E  Q  T
T  U  H  D  Z  Y  J  H  V
W  E  X  Z  N  I  C  K  Y
```

LORNA

ANNE

MARIA

107 Puppy love

Help the dog through the maze to its puppies by following the numbers in the six times table.

108 Fun on the farm

Look carefully at these two pictures.
There are seven differences. Can you spot them?

109 Fairground fun
Unscramble the names of these fairground rides.

ibg elhew

elhert-sltkere

upebrm rcsa

ermyr-og-dunor

110 Odd apples

Count the apples on the trees. Circle the trees that have
an ODD number of apples.

111 Crossword of colours

The pictures of these things are clues to the colours. Look at the example.
Follow the numbers across and down, and write the words in the grid.

7

2

1

5

6

4 p u r p l e

5

6

4 →

4 ↓

7

3

112 **Frosty fun**

Help the children to get through the maze to the snowman.

113 **Flutter-by butterfly**

Draw lines to match the pairs of butterflies that are the same.

114 Ahoy there!

Follow the lines from the pirates to see who has got the crown.

115 Odd one out

Look at each row of objects.
Put a tick next to the picture that is the odd one out in each row.

116 Missing middles

These words are missing their middle letters.
Complete the words using the pictures as clues.

pu＿＿et

ca＿＿ot

pi＿＿ow

ke＿＿le

117 **Fruity code**

Use the code to work out the answers to the sums.

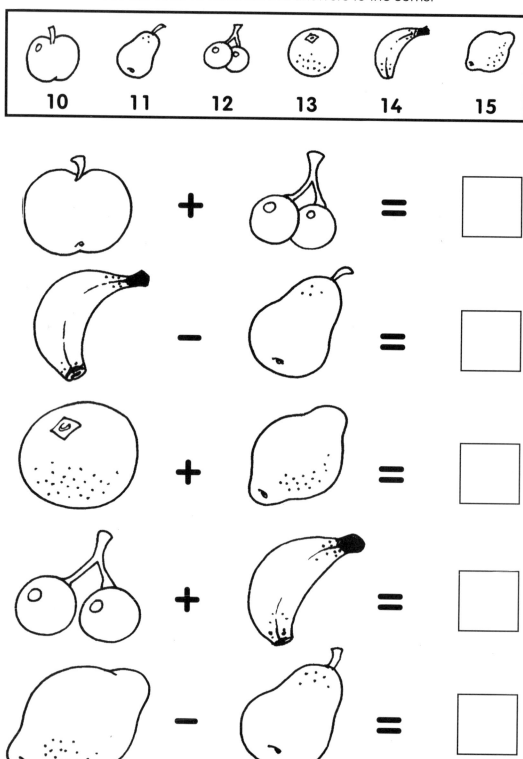

118 Race to the finish

Look at the symbols in the box. Each symbol represents a different number of minutes. Add up the times to see who is the slowest.

119 Addition

Do these addition sums.

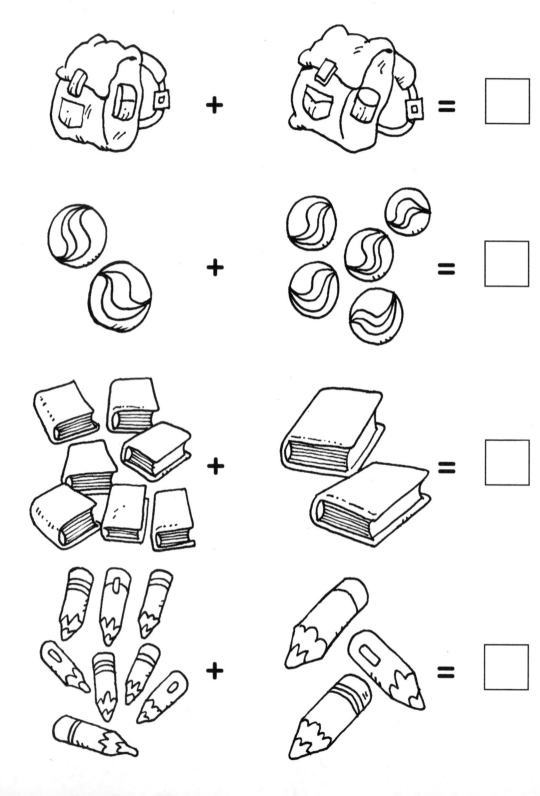

120 Clothing scramble

Unscramble the letters to spell the words.
Write the correct spelling on the lines.

rdses

dress

sreourst

trousers

rsthi

shirts

hoses

shoes

koscs

socks

isrkt

skirt

121 Sums puzzles

Do the sums in the grids by filling in the missing numbers.

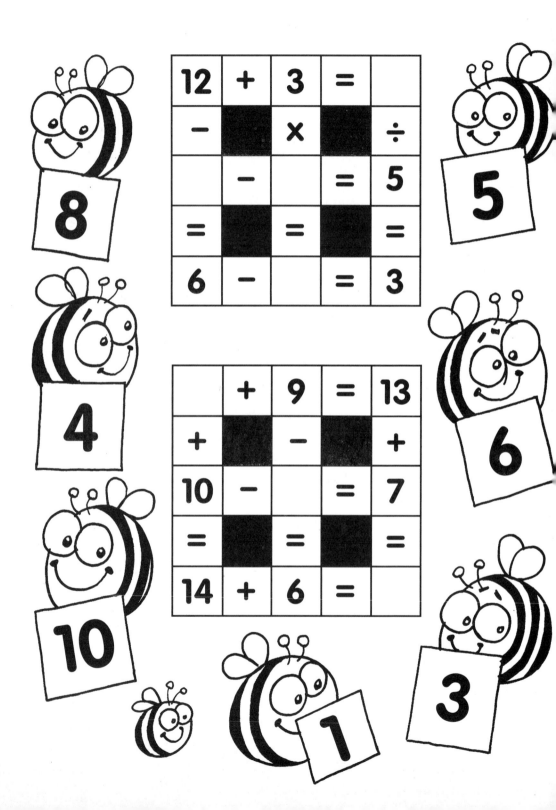

12	+	3	=	
−		×		÷
	−		=	5
=		=		=
6	−		=	3

8

5

4

6

	+	9	=	13
+		−		+
10	−		=	7
=		=		=
14	+	6	=	

10

3

1

122 Picture wheel

Write the first letter of each picture in the space in the centre of the picture wheel. You will spell the name of a tiny creature.

123 **Longer words**

Draw lines to join two words to make longer words.

honey

tooth

stair

goose

case

berries

moon

brush

124 **All aboard**

Starting with the letter 'a', draw a line to join the dots
and complete the picture.

125 Number patterns

Look at the numbers in the ladders and write
in the missing numbers.

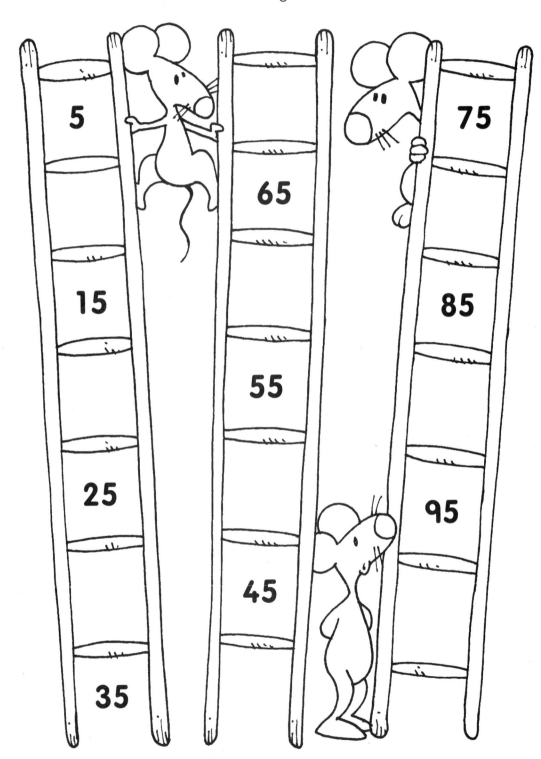

126 Spotty-cow sums

Count the spots on the cows and write the numbers in the daisies.
Then do the multiplication sums.

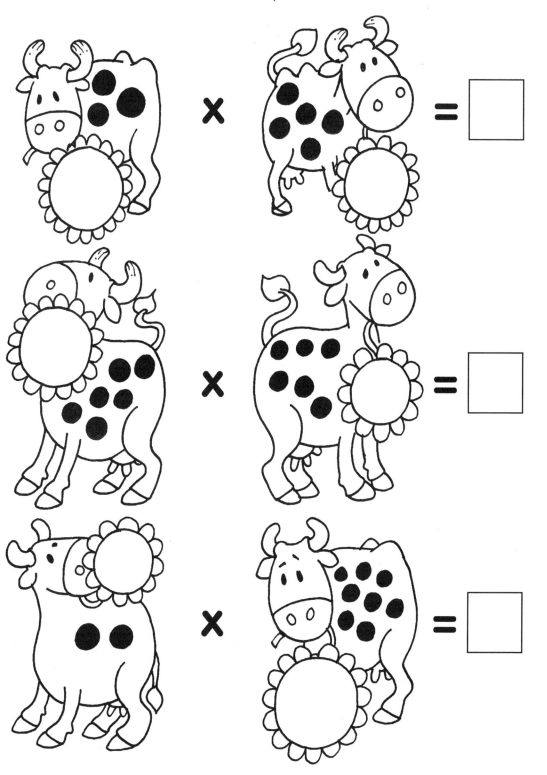

127 The least rabbits

Count the number of baby rabbits each mother rabbit has.
Circle the mother with the LEAST baby rabbits.

128 Heads and tails

Write the first letter of each picture in the boxes.
You will make a new word.

☐ e a ☐

☐ a i ☐

☐ t e ☐

☐ g g ☐

129 **Fishing silhouettes**

Draw lines to match the gnomes with their silhouettes.

130 Party madness

Look at the picture and find eight things that have gone wrong.

131 Copy and draw

Copying square by square, use the grid to help you draw this picture.

132 Subtraction sums

Do these sums.

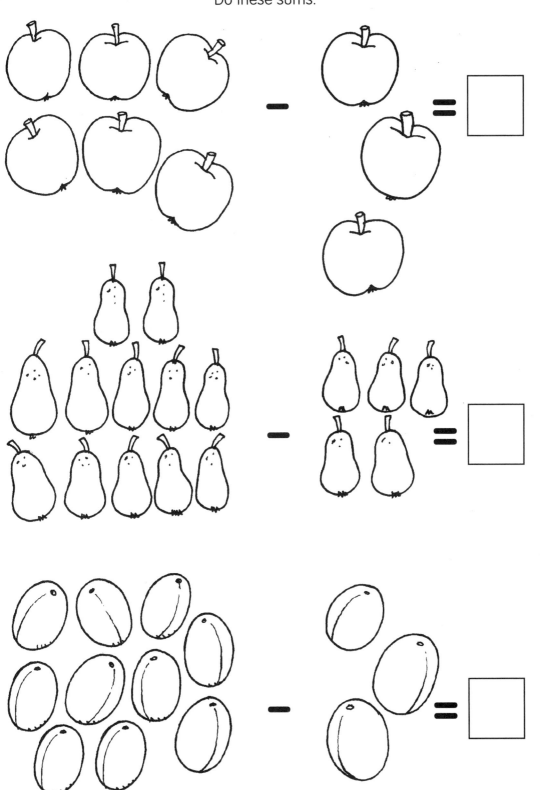

133 Plural endings

Tick the correct spelling of the plurals below.

foot

☐ foots
☐ feet

mouse

☐ mice
☐ mouses

spy

☐ spyes
☐ spies

goose

☐ geese
☐ gooses

scarf

☐ scarfs
☐ scarves

134 What is it?

Starting with the letter 'm', cross out every other letter to spell a word.
Write the word on the line.

msonhoewdfclxasktey

_____

135 What a catch!

Look at the pictures and work out the correct order of this story.
Write the numbers 1 to 4 in the boxes.

136 Word trail

Use the picture clues to fill in the word trail. The last letter of each word is the first letter of the next word.

137 New words

How many new words can you make from the word 'tortoise'?
Write the new words in the tortoise's shell.

tortoise

138 Letter codes

Using the code in the box as a guide, fill in the missing letters
to spell a sea creature.

	1	2	3	4	5	6
A	q	e	a	u	p	r
B	a	i	t	u	o	e
C	u	c	b	i	h	v
D	o	r	x	c	z	r
E	w	l	u	f	y	p
F	v	s	n	o	e	k

__ __ __ __ __ __ __

B5   D4   B3   D1   E6   E3   F2

139 Adding a letter

Add a letter to these words to make new words.

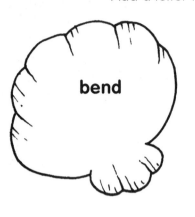

bend + | l | =

bob + | m | =

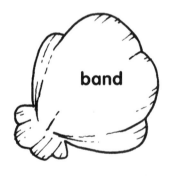

band + | r | =

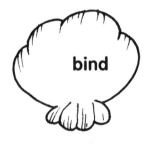

bind + | l | =

140 **Trivia**

What is a meat-eating animal called?
- a. a carnivore
- b. a herbivore
- c. a canine

141 **Trivia**

What is a thesaurus?
- a. a book of words
- b. a type of magician
- c. a plant-eating dinosaur

142 Dividing

Do these division sums and draw lines to match the answers with the correct group below.

$$12 \div 3 = \boxed{}$$

$$25 \div 5 = \boxed{}$$

$$81 \div 9 = \boxed{}$$

$$100 \div 10 = \boxed{}$$

143 Missing hands

Draw the hands on the faces of these clocks.

2.30

1.45

quarter-to eight

three o'clock

144 Hidden names

In each grid, cross out the letters that appear more than once to discover the hidden names. Write the names on the lines.

O	E	U	S	W
R	G	N	M	T
I	W	C	O	Z
S	K	U	R	E
T	M	Z	Y	G

_____

S	U	P	T	G
L	K	E	Y	M
T	U	I	J	S
N	G	Y	D	M
E	P	A	J	K

_____

145 Counting in the garden

Look carefully at this picture. How many different things can you count?
Write the answers in the boxes.

tortoises	butterflies	flower pots	bees	flower petals

146 Word scrambles

There are two words hidden in each row of scrambled letters.
The pictures are clues to the words. Write the words on the lines.

 **eskghnprintics**

_____   _____

 **bpanaapnale**

_____   _____

 **bsoebraithr**

_____   _____

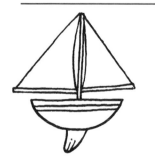 **tancoeboa**

_____   _____

147 Shape spellings

Tick the correct spelling for each of the shapes.

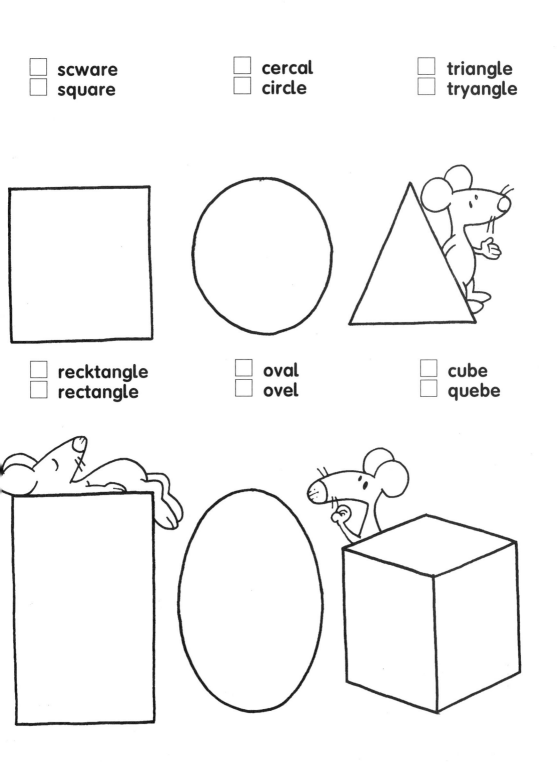

☐ scware
☐ square

☐ cercal
☐ circle

☐ triangle
☐ tryangle

☐ recktangle
☐ rectangle

☐ oval
☐ ovel

☐ cube
☐ quebe

148 Mini beasts wordsearch

Look in the wordsearch grid for eight mini beasts.
You will find them by reading across or down.
Draw a ring around the words as you find them.

W	A	A	S	J	S	G	L	J
X	S	N	A	I	L	K	A	X
J	K	T	I	A	U	D	D	T
B	V	N	P	B	G	B	Y	F
W	O	R	M	E	Q	T	B	E
P	Q	Z	A	E	F	D	I	A
W	Z	X	G	T	J	X	R	R
U	D	P	F	L	B	Y	D	W
S	P	I	D	E	R	K	N	I
R	S	Y	Z	H	L	O	P	G

149 **Leap frog**

Help the frog to leap through the maze to the lily pad by following the numbers that divide exactly by three.

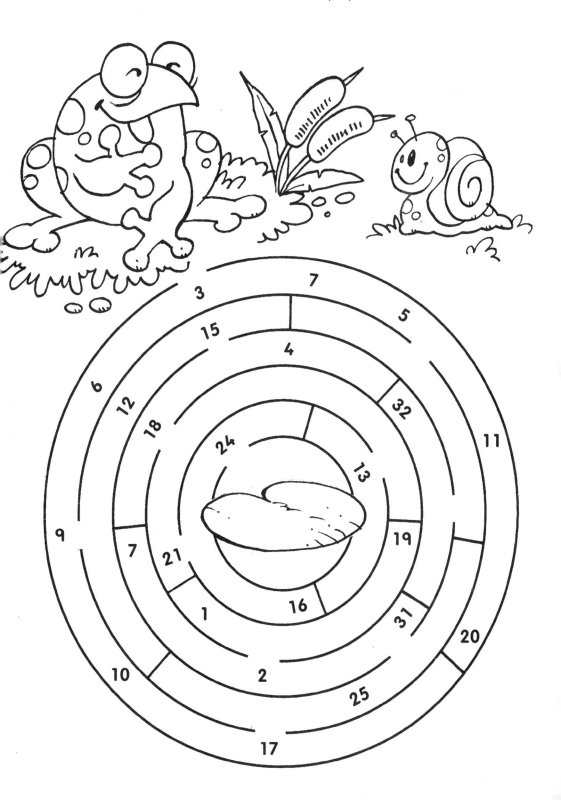

150 Ball skills

Look carefully at these two pictures.
There are 10 differences. Can you spot them?

151 At the airport
Unscramble the names of these countries.

Mexico

Japan

Canada

Australia

New Zealand

China

India

ACANAD

RSTAALIUA

NWE LEANDZA

AHICN

ADINI

IXCOEM

ANJPA

152 **Even eggs**

Count the eggs in the nests. Circle the nests that have
an EVEN number of eggs.

153 Yummy crossword

These pictures of food are clues to the words.
Follow the numbers across and down, and write the words in the grid.

154 Ahoy there!

Help the pirate ship to get through the maze to the island.

155 Dinosaur twins

Draw lines to match the pairs of dinosaurs that are the same.

156 In the dog house

Follow the leads from the dogs to see who lives in each kennel.

157 Odd one out

Look at each row of objects.
Put a tick next to the picture that is the odd one out in each row.

158 Missing letters

These words are missing some letters.
Complete the words using the pictures as clues.

squid

strawberry

squirrel

skates

159 Flower sums

Count the petals on the flowers and write the numbers in the centres.
Then do the multiplication sums.

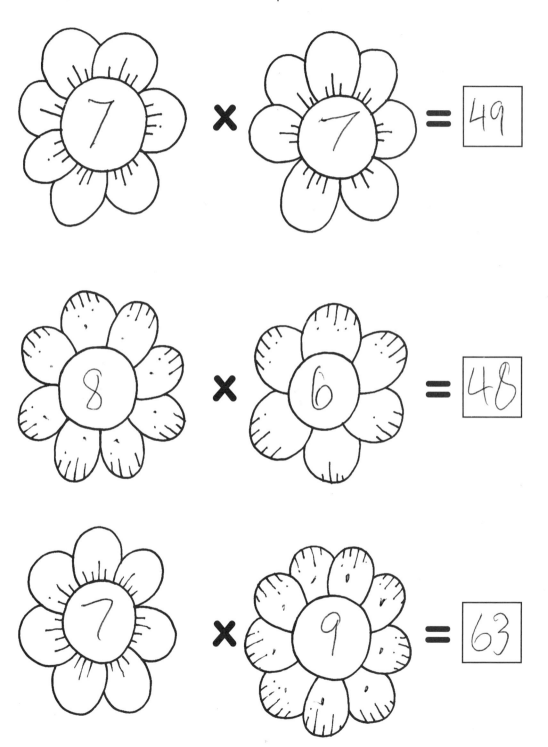

7 × 7 = 49

8 × 6 = 48

7 × 9 = 63

160 On the slopes

Look at the symbols in the box. Each symbol represents a different number of minutes. Add up the times to see which skier finishes first.

161 Addition

Do these addition sums.

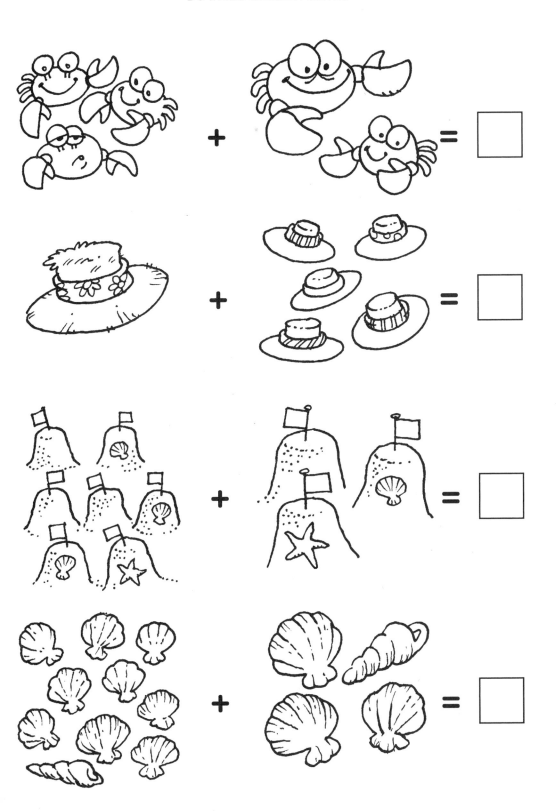

162 Pond-life scramble

Unscramble the letters to spell the words.
Write the correct spelling on the lines.

ilnucdgk

_____

gorf

_____

lrefsow

_____

dbegri

_____

nasw

_____

eosog

_____

163 Sums puzzles

Do the sums in the grids by filling in the missing numbers.

12	+	4	=	
−		+		−
10	−		=	8
=		=		=
2	+	6	=	

	+	11	=	16
+		+		+
6	+		=	9
=		=		=
11	+	14	=	

164 Picture wheel

Write the first letter of each picture in the space in the centre of the picture wheel. You will spell the name of some friendly sea creatures.

165 Longer words

Draw lines to join two words to make longer words.

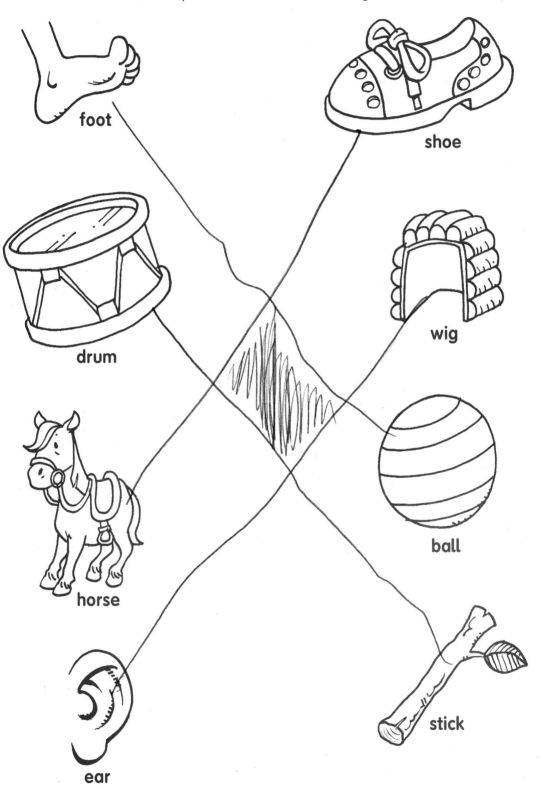

foot

shoe

drum

wig

horse

ball

ear

stick

166 Fun in the sand

Starting with the letter 'a', draw a line to join the dots
and complete the picture.

167 Number patterns

Look at the numbers in the worms and write
in the missing numbers.

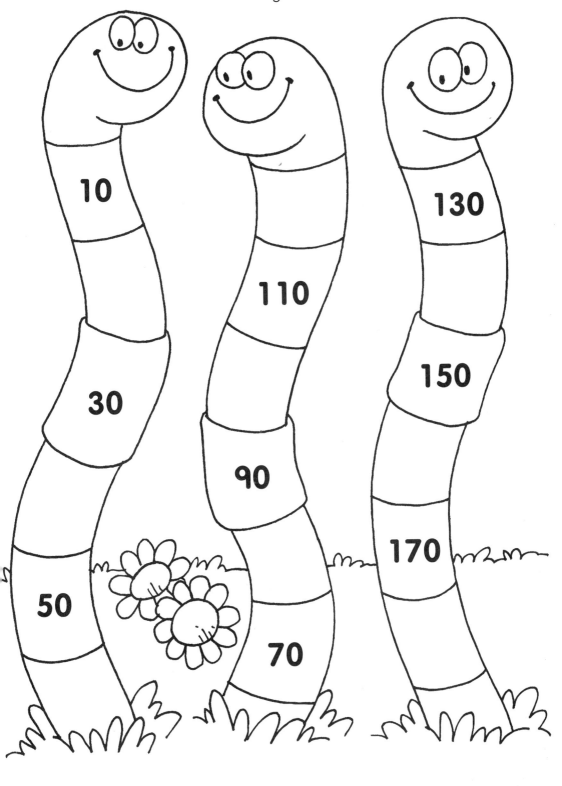

168 A lot of legs sums

Count the legs on the creatures and write the numbers in their bodies.
Then do the multiplication sums.

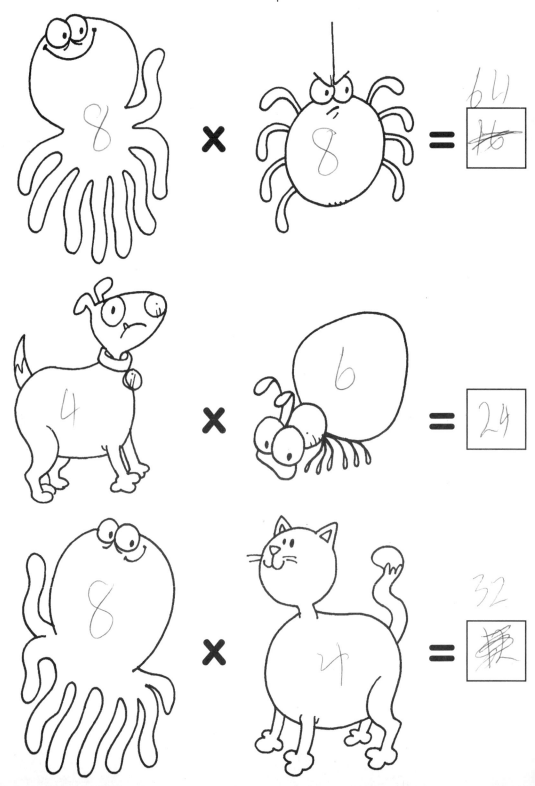

169 The most stripes

Count the number of stripes each zebra has.
Circle the zebra with the MOST stripes.

170 **Heads and tails**

Write the first letter of each picture in the boxes.
You will make a new word.

☐ a i ☐

☐ a k ☐

☐ e l ☐

☐ o o ☐

171 Dancing silhouettes

Draw lines to match the ballerinas with their silhouettes.

172 Crazy camping

Look at the picture and find eight things that have gone wrong.

173 Copy and draw

Copying square by square, use the grid to help you draw
the other half of this pilot in his flying machine.

174 Subtraction sums

Do these sums.

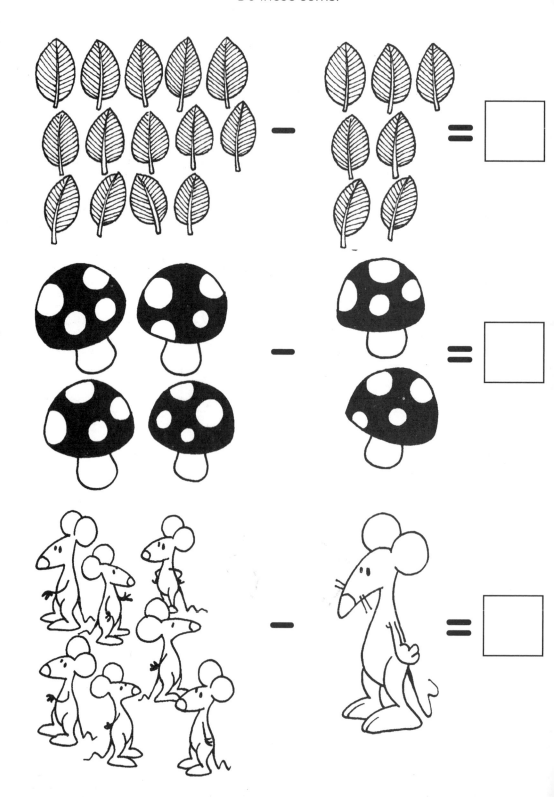

175 Make it plural

Write the plural spellings for each of these words.

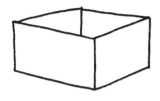

box

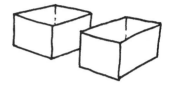

_____

tiger

_____

potato

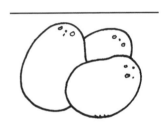

_____

scarecrow

_____

bus

_____

176 What is it?

Starting with the letter 'n', cross out every other letter to spell a word.
Write the word on the line.

nmioptkolrsbaiqkvec

_____

177 An alien encounter

Look at the pictures and work out the correct order of this story.
Write the numbers 1 to 4 in the boxes.

178 Word trail

Use the picture clues to fill in the word trail. The last letter of each word is the first letter of the next word.

179 New words

How many new words can you make from the word 'lighthouse'?
Write the new words in the lighthouse.

lighthouse

light, house
hot, use, hit
ghost, goes
hut, gut
sight, hog
site, ties, hole
sole, soil, toil
slot, slit, shot
slight, stole, silt
tot, slut,

180 Letter codes

Using the code in the box as a guide, fill in the missing letters to spell a type of building.

	1	**2**	**3**	**4**	**5**	**6**
A	t	q	w	s	e	d
B	z	x	c	s	b	n
C	m	l	p	o	k	l
D	u	a	g	h	c	f
E	r	e	s	w	c	z
F	v	c	e	b	m	r

__ __ __ __ __ __
D5 D2 B4 A1 C6 F3

181 Taking away 'e'

Take away 'e' from these words to make new words.

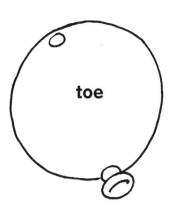 **toe** - $\boxed{e}$ =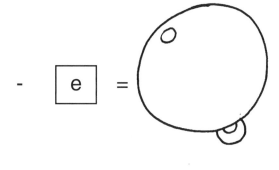

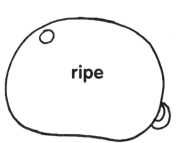 **ripe** - $\boxed{e}$ =

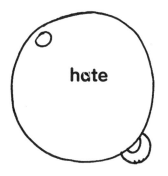 **hate** - $\boxed{e}$ =

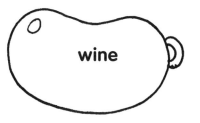 **wine** - $\boxed{e}$ =

182 Trivia
Which of these is an extinct bird?
a. a dodo
b. a mojo
c. a hobo

183 Trivia
What is a baby kangaroo called?
a. a hopper
b. a joey
c. a wallaby

184 Dividing

Do these division sums and draw lines to match the answers
with the correct group below.

$$32 \div 4 = \boxed{}$$

$$56 \div 8 = \boxed{}$$

$$33 \div 11 = \boxed{}$$

$$30 \div 2 = \boxed{}$$

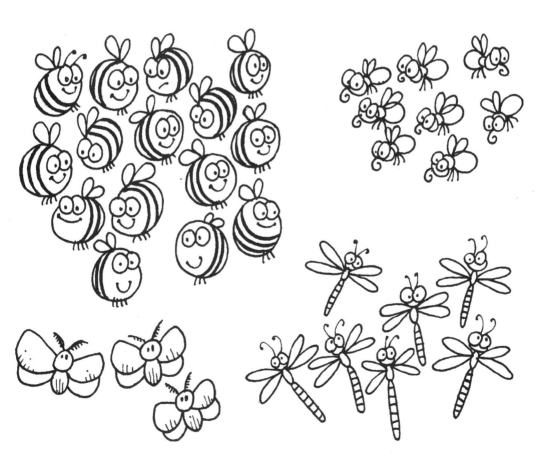

185 Tell the time

What time does each clock say? Write it on the line.

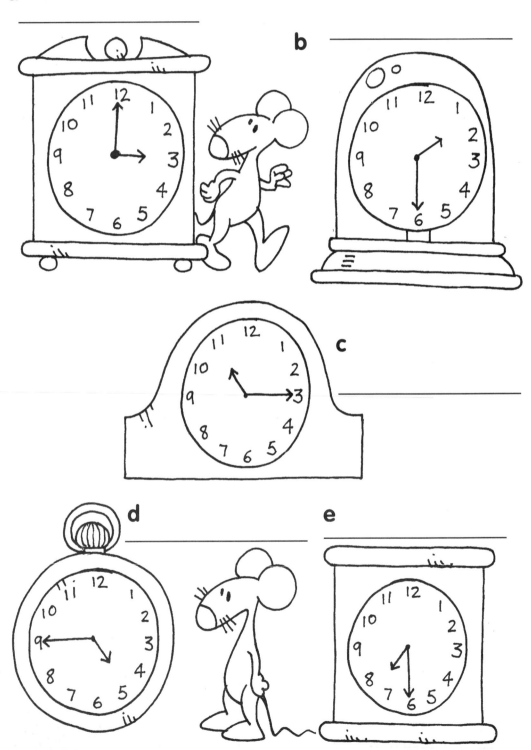

a

_____

b _____

c _____

d _____

e _____

186 Hidden names

In each grid, cross out the letters that appear more than once to discover the hidden names. Write the names on the lines.

E	R	L	G	F
S	A	B	V	I
T	M	F	H	E
R	B	T	O	L
V	N	G	H	A

_____

H	M	A	C	N
D	I	B	Q	Y
O	K	Y	G	H
E	C	M	B	K
A	Q	O	D	L

_____

187 Counting in space

Look carefully at this picture. How many different things can you count?
Write the answers in the boxes.

astronauts	rockets	spaceships	planets	stars

188 Word scrambles

There are two words hidden in each row of scrambled letters.
The pictures are clues to the words. Write the words on the lines.

ohuecesesem

cheese

mouse

inrprobotar

parrot

robin

rbsahkacr

shark

crab

yuapdstlii

189 Pet spellings

Tick the correct spelling for each of the pictures.

☐ goaldfish
☐ goldfish

☐ hamstar
☐ hamster

☐ parrot
☐ parot

☐ hoarse
☐ horse

☐ rabbit
☐ rabit

☐ puppey
☐ puppy

190 Boys' names wordsearch

Look in the wordsearch grid for the names of these eight boys.
You will find them by reading across or down.
Draw a ring around the words as you find them.

ANDREW

DANIEL

MARTIN

RICHARD

JOHN

```
Y  N  B  M  A  R  K  A  J
A  X  S  A  B  J  U  J  A
V  E  Q  R  J  O  H  N  N
Y  D  X  T  Y  U  X  N  D
T  A  Q  I  Q  V  J  H  R
O  N  U  N  T  W  Q  I  E
R  I  C  H  A  R  D  A  W
H  E  S  S  G  B  H  N  N
Q  L  Y  E  P  T  Z  V  N
X  S  T  U  A  R  T  H  P
```

MARK

STUART

IAN

191 **Lost eggs**

Help the birds through the maze to their nest by following
the numbers that divide exactly by two.

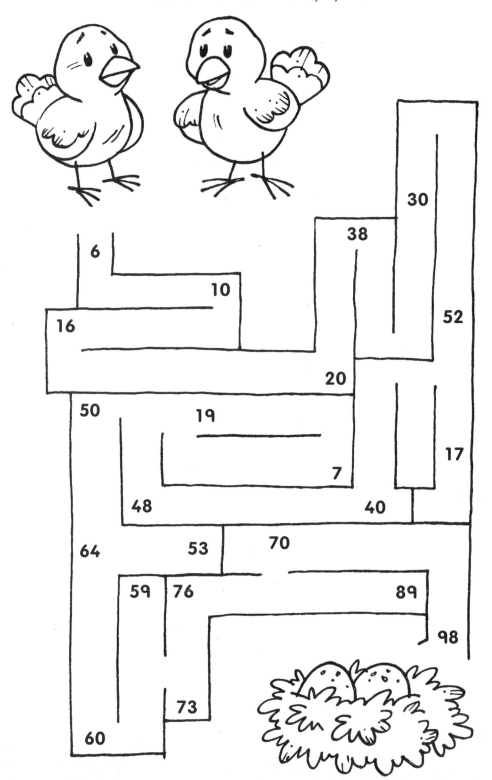

192 Race to the finish

Look carefully at these two pictures.
There are 10 differences. Can you spot them?

193 Seeing sights

Unscramble the names of these city sights.

umsume

atr alerylg

lceast

taestu

194 **Odd sweets**

Count the sweets in the jars. Circle the jars that have
an ODD number of sweets.

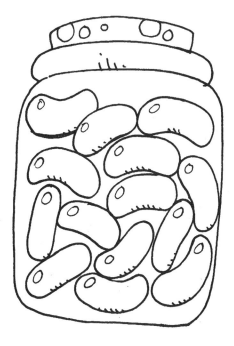

195 Ball code

Use the code to work out the answers to the sums.

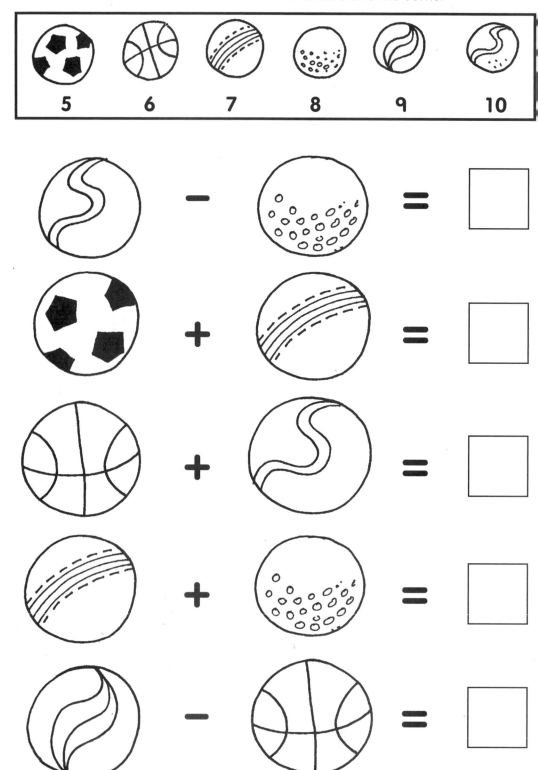

196 Missing letters

These words are missing some letters.
Complete the words using the pictures as clues.

_ _apes

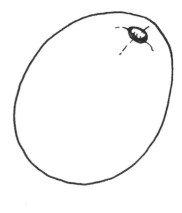

_ _um

_ _own

_ _ink

197 **Odd one out**

Look at each row of objects.
Put a tick next to the picture that is the odd one out in each row.

198 **Whose hat?**

Follow the lines from the people to see who owns each hat.

199 Up, up and away

Draw lines to match the pairs of balloons that are the same.

200 Mermaid maze

Help the mermaid to get through the maze to her cave.

201 **Up a tree crossword**

The pictures of things you might find in a tree are clues to the words.
Follow the numbers across and down, and write the words in the grid.

¹c	²a	t	
	p		
	p		
	l		

³m o n ⁴k e y

⁵6

⁶s q u i r r ⁷e l

r e

d a

t v

e

⁸n e a t

202 Number patterns

Look at the numbers in the balls and write
in the missing numbers.

203 **Happy birthday**

Starting with the letter 'a', draw a line to join the dots
and complete the picture.

204 **Outer space**

Draw lines to join the rockets to the planets to make longer words.

205 Picture wheel

Write the first letter of each picture in the space in the centre of the picture wheel. You will spell the name of a vegetable.

206 Sums puzzles

Do the sums in the grids by filling in the missing numbers.

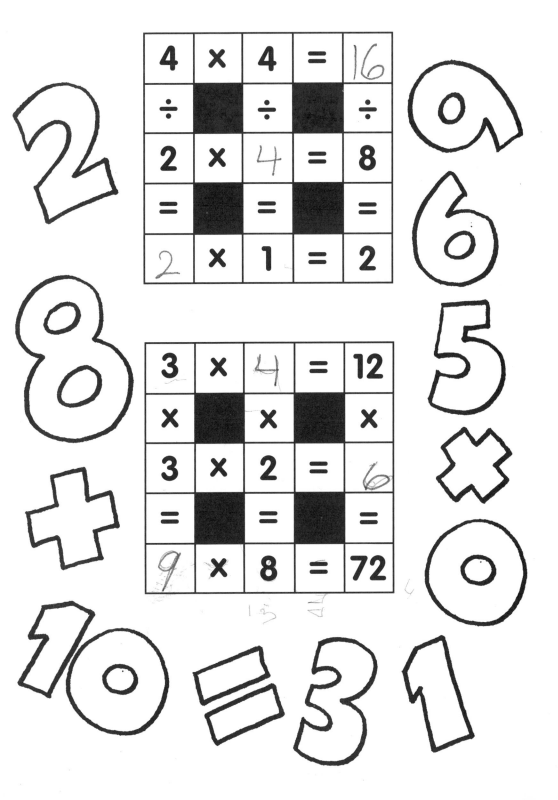

Grid 1:

4	×	4	=	16
÷		÷		÷
2	×	4	=	8
=		=		=
2	×	1	=	2

Grid 2:

3	×	4	=	12
×		×		×
3	×	2	=	6
=		=		=
9	×	8	=	72

207 Addition

Do these addition sums.

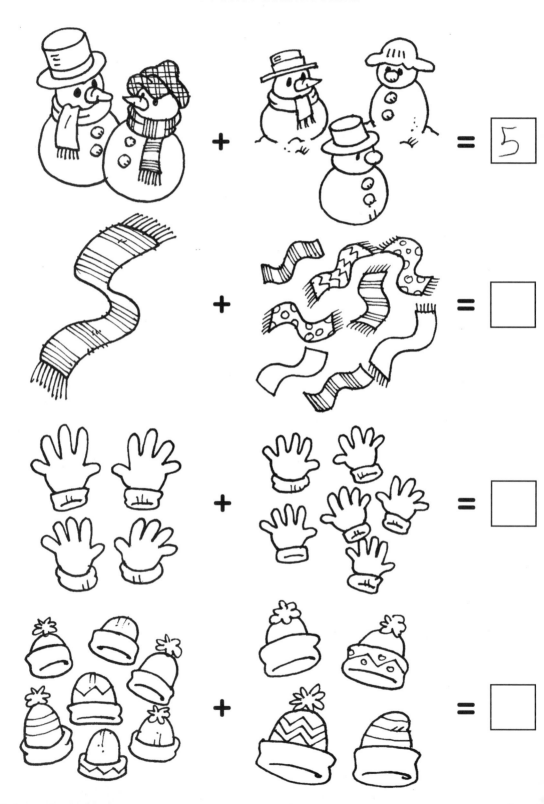

208 Fast lane

Look at the symbols in the box. Each symbol represents a different number of minutes. Add up the times to see which swimmer wins the race.

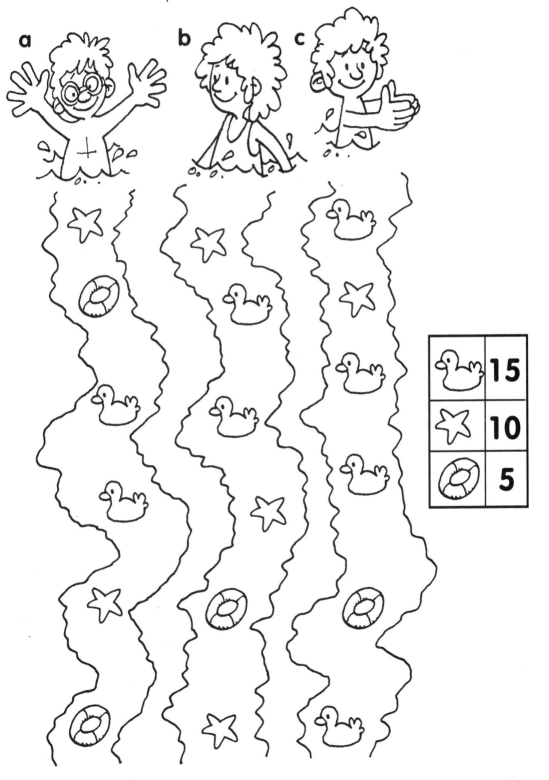

209 Make it plural

Write the plural spellings for each of these words.

sandcastle

sandcastle _____

bush

bushes _____

candle

4 candles _____

glass

glasses _____

elephant

elephants _____

210 Subtraction sums

Do these sums.

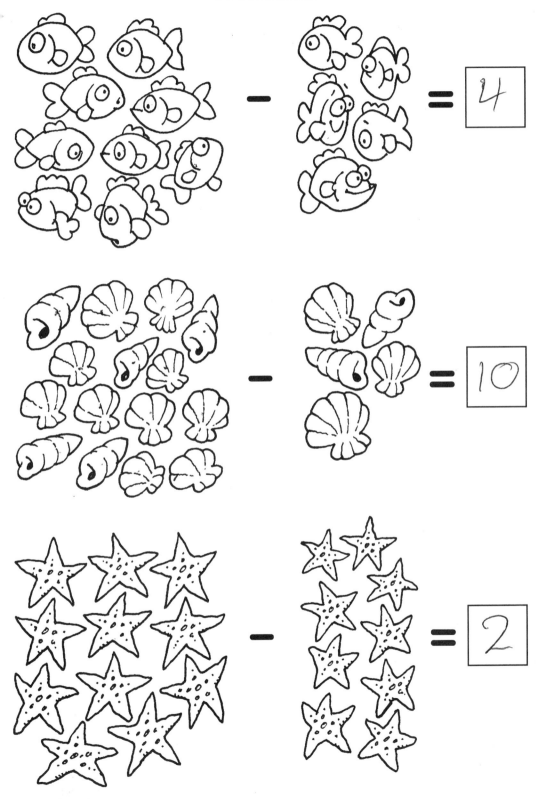

211 Clown shadow

Can you match the clown with his shadow?

212 Heads and tails

Write the first letter of each picture in the boxes.
You will make a new word.

 $\boxed{T}$ u l i $\boxed{P}$

 $\boxed{H}$ e a r $\boxed{T}$

 $\boxed{C}$ h e a $\boxed{P}$

 $\boxed{O}$ r d e $\boxed{r}$

213 T-shirt sums

What number does each child have on their t-shirt?
Write the numbers on the flags, then do the sums.

214 Trivia

What is a baby whale called?
a. a cow
b. a calf
c. a pup

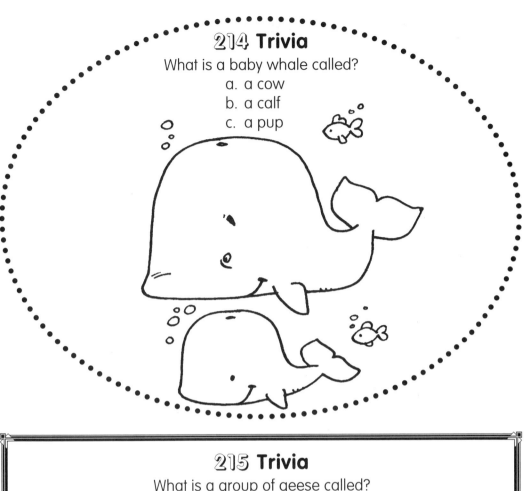

215 Trivia

What is a group of geese called?
a. a giggle
b. a gaggle
c. a goggle

Using the code in the box as a guide, fill in the missing letters
to spell something on a farm.

	1	2	3	4	5	6
A	l	k	h	g	f	d
B	s	a	q	w	p	c
C	i	u	y	t	r	t
D	z	m	x	n	b	c
E	v	r	f	s	a	o
F	o	p	r	t	y	r

t	r	a	c	t	o	r
C4	F3	B2	B6	C6	E6	F3

217 New words

How many new words can you make from the word 'aeroplane'?
Write the new words in the clouds.

aeroplane

218 **Word trail**

Use the picture clues to fill in the word trail. The last letter of each word is the first letter of the next word.

219 Birthday surprises

Look at the pictures and work out the correct order of this story.
Write the numbers 1 to 4 in the boxes.

220 What is it?

Starting with the letter 'g', cross out every other letter to spell a word.
Write the word on the line.

ghlahmgsdtwenro

_____

221 **Cinderella**

Look at the pictures and work out the correct order of this story.
Write the numbers 1 to 4 in the boxes.

222 Word trail

Use the picture clues to fill in the word trail. The last letter of each word
is the first letter of the next word.

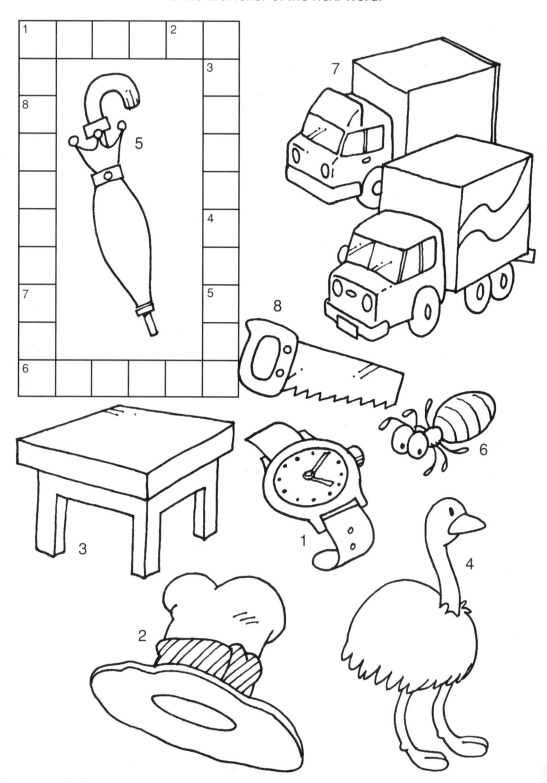

223 New words

How many new words can you make from the word 'sunflower'?
Write the new words in the centre of the flower.

sunflower

run
fun
sun
flower
wolf
slow

224 Letter codes

Using the code in the box as a guide, fill in the missing letters to spell something magical.

	1	2	3	4	5	6
A	i	k	g	o	p	z
B	d	c	e	r	a	m
C	r	h	r	l	d	c
D	f	p	x	d	i	o
E	g	y	f	k	u	w
F	a	z	c	f	a	w

w i z a r d

F6 A1 A6 F1 C3 C5

225 Hidden words

In each grid, cross out the letters that appear more than once to discover the hidden words. Write the words on the lines.

e	t	c	h	i
a	o	b	k	m
u	h	n	b	e
i	c	w	u	t
l	n	k	m	a

_____

c	g	i	k	m
b	n	s	o	w
d	w	a	v	c
g	s	i	o	v
m	t	k	d	n

_____

226 Tell the time

What time does each clock say? Write it on the line.

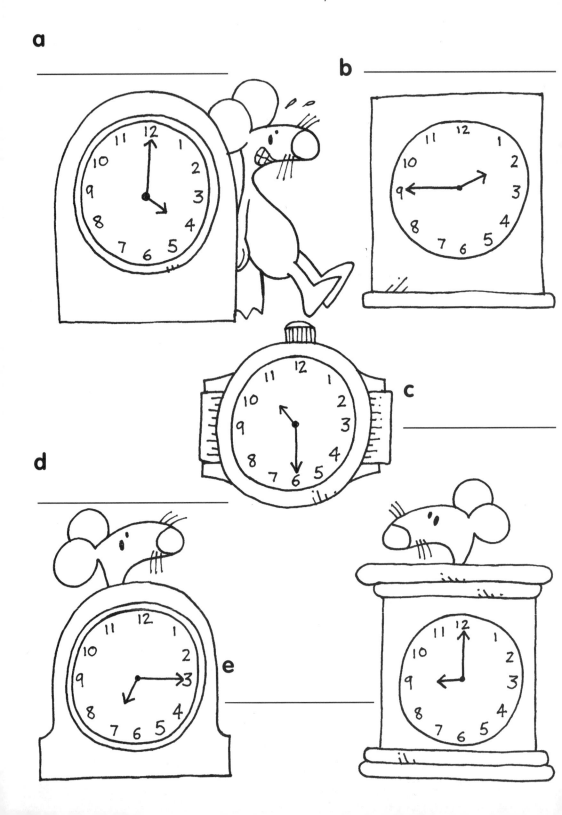

a _____

b _____

c _____

d _____

e _____

227 **Dividing**

Do these division sums and draw lines to match the answers
with the correct group below.

$36 \div 6 =$ ☐

$45 \div 5 =$ ☐

$24 \div 8 =$ ☐

$12 \div 12 =$ ☐

228 Trivia

Who invented the electric light bulb?
- a. Thomas Edison
- b. James Watt
- c. Benjamin Bright

229 Trivia

What is a roof made
of woven straw called?
- a. patched
- b. thatched
- c. hatched

230 Counting in the classroom

Look carefully at this picture. How many different things can you count?
Write the answers in the boxes.

bags   children   teachers   books   pencils

231 Word scrambles

There are two words hidden in each row of scrambled letters.
The pictures are clues to the words. Write the words on the lines.

 **tlaouwstncnaro**

_____   _____

 **ionteroevistolb**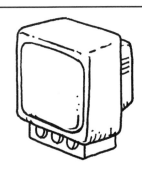

_____   _____

 **epdasaknan**

_____   _____

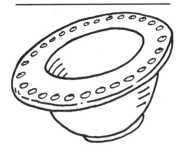 **oteblplaw**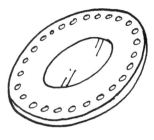

_____   _____

232 Lunch-box spellings

Tick the correct spelling for each of the pictures.

☐ cake
☐ cayke

☐ sandwich
☐ sandwitch

☐ orange
☐ oranje

☐ chocalat
☐ chocolate

☐ appel
☐ apple

☐ crisps
☐ krisps

233 Sporty wordsearch

Look in the wordsearch grid for eight sports.
You will find them by reading across or down.
Draw a ring around the words as you find them.

B	A	S	E	B	A	L	L	N
Q	R	U	N	N	I	N	G	E
S	K	I	I	N	G	T	H	T
W	J	B	Y	R	T	Y	U	B
I	O	Z	G	A	F	S	W	A
M	F	O	O	T	B	A	L	L
M	G	V	L	T	E	J	M	L
I	U	D	F	F	G	B	P	I
N	W	T	E	N	N	I	S	X
G	N	S	E	Q	D	Y	S	H

234 Monster of the deep

Help the sea monster back to his cave by following
the numbers in the seven times table.

235 Gone fishing

Look carefully at these two pictures.
There are 10 differences. Can you spot them?

236 Treasure island crossword

The pictures of things on a treasure island are clues to the words.
Follow the numbers across and down, and write the words in the grid.

237 Bee trouble

Help the lost bee to get through the maze to the hive.

238 Alien adventures

Follow the lines to see which spaceship each alien has.

239 Odd one out

Look at each row of objects.
Put a tick next to the picture that is the odd one out in each row.

240 Missing letters

These words are missing some letters.
Complete the words using the pictures as clues.

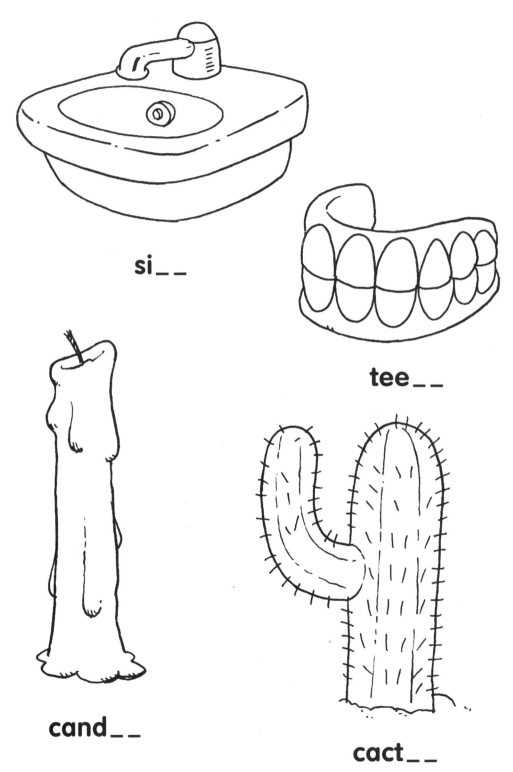

si_ _

tee_ _

cand_ _

cact_ _

241 Footwear code

Use the code to work out the answers to the sums.

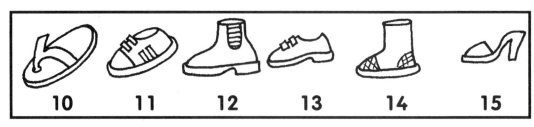

10	11	12	13	14	15

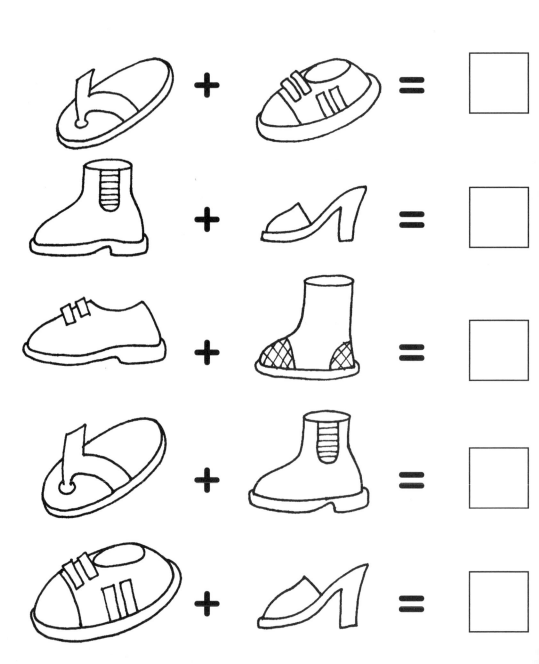

242 On your marks

Look at the symbols in the box. Each symbol represents a different number of minutes. Add up the times to see who wins the sack race.

243 Adding-up spines

Count the spines on the dinosaurs and write the numbers in the boxes. Then do the sum.

☐ + ☐ + ☐ + ☐ + ☐

= ☐ spines altogether

244 Sums puzzles

Do the sums in the grids by filling in the missing numbers.

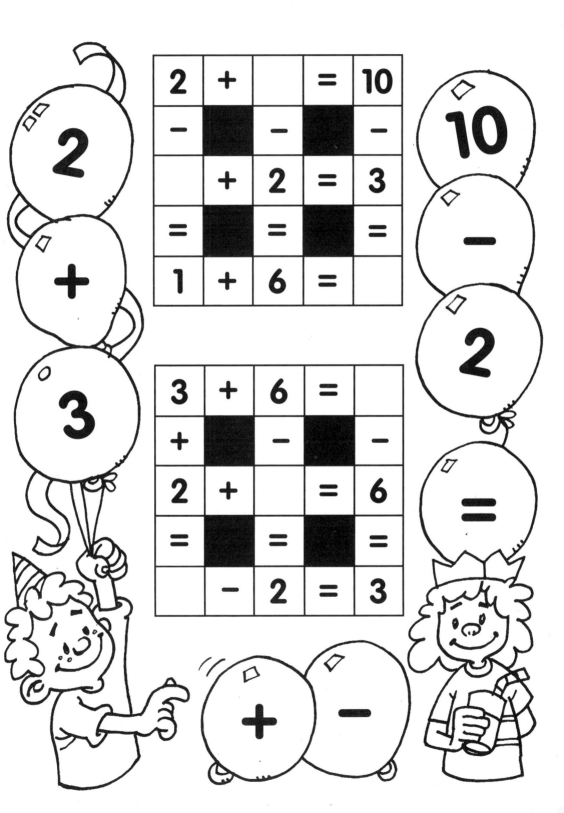

Grid 1:

2	+		=	10
-		-		-
	+	2	=	3
=		=		=
1	+	6	=	

Grid 2:

3	+	6	=	
+		-		-
2	+		=	6
=		=		=
	-	2	=	3

245 Picture wheel

Write the first letter of each picture in the space in the centre of the picture wheel. You will spell the name of something nice to give!

246 Oranges and lemons

Draw lines to join the oranges to the lemons to make longer words.

finger

pet

car

lace

gold

print

neck

fish

247 Who scares the crows?

Starting with number 1, draw a line to join the dots and complete the picture.

248 Number patterns

Look at the numbers in the flags and write
in the missing numbers.

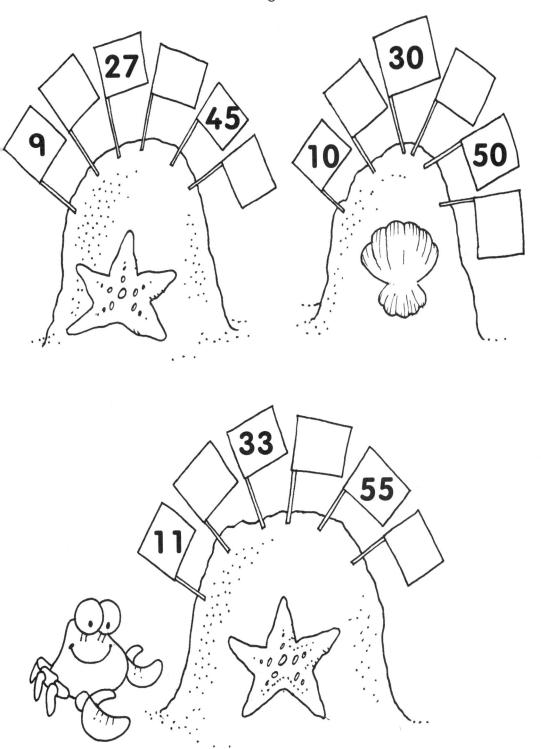

249 Sum snakes

Do the multiplication sums in these snakes.

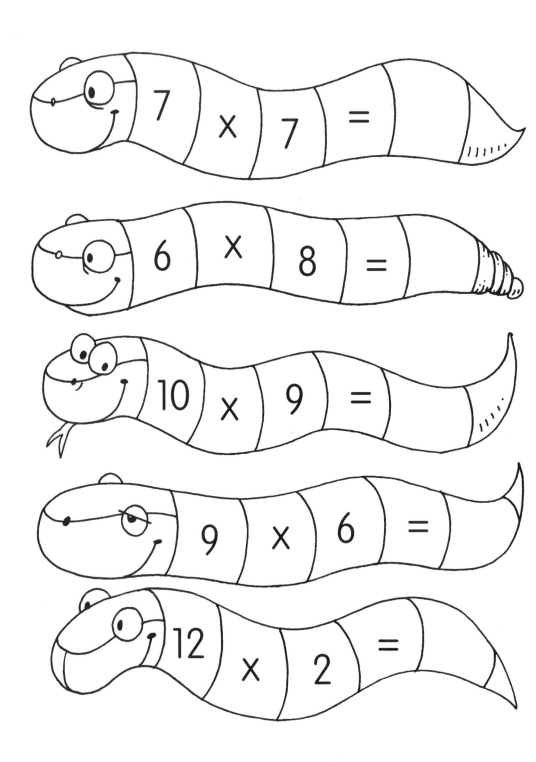

$7 \times 7 =$

$6 \times 8 =$

$10 \times 9 =$

$9 \times 6 =$

$12 \times 2 =$

250 **Heads and tails**

Write the first letter of each picture in the boxes.
You will make a new word.

☐ l i n ☐

☐ e a r ☐

☐ e a r ☐

☐ l o o ☐

Can you match the witch with her shadow?

252 Skateboard sums

Do these subtraction sums.
Join the sums to the answers.

253 What is it?

Starting with the letter 'f', cross out every other letter to spell a toy.
Write the words on the line.

ftgeudbdmys boepaqrf

_____

254 What's hatching?

Look at the pictures and work out the correct order of this story.
Write the numbers 1 to 4 in the boxes.

255 Word trail

Use the picture clues to fill in the word trail. The last letter of each word is the first letter of the next word.

256 New words

How many new words can you make from the word 'starfish'?
Write the new words in the starfish and shells.

starfish

257 Letter codes

Using the code in the box as a guide, fill in the missing letters to spell something at a party.

	1	2	3	4	5	6
A	r	q	w	c	d	n
B	a	o	u	i	o	e
C	y	h	b	g	s	l
D	x	c	v	b	y	l
E	a	e	f	b	t	l
F	e	o	p	c	i	b

___ ___ ___ ___ ___ ___ ___
E4   E1   C6   D6   B2   F2   A6

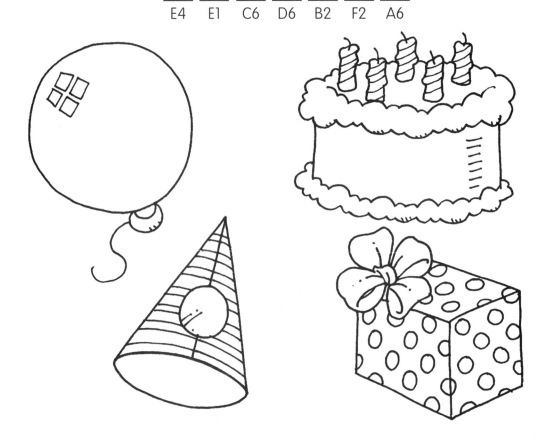

258 Dividing

Do these division sums and draw lines to match the answers with the correct group below.

$$28 \div 7 = \boxed{}$$

$$30 \div 6 = \boxed{}$$

$$18 \div 9 = \boxed{}$$

$$99 \div 9 = \boxed{}$$

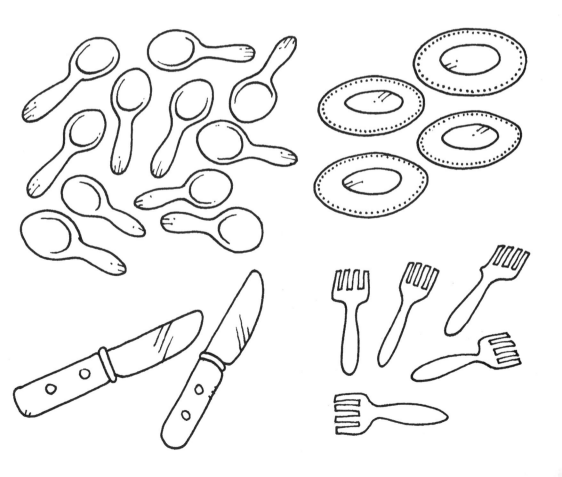

259 Hidden words

In each grid, cross out the letters that appear more than once to discover the hidden words. Write the words on the lines.

o	p	y	r	m
u	t	s	h	o
v	r	p	g	a
i	y	a	c	e
v	e	h	g	t

_____

n	p	i	o	l
m	r	l	c	e
o	n	a	i	b
t	i	i	h	r
e	s	b	p	c

_____

260 Counting on a picnic

Look carefully at this picture. How many different things can you count?
Write the answers in the boxes.

bottles	sandwiches	baskets	cakes	apples

261 Word scrambles

There are two words hidden in each row of scrambled letters.
The pictures are clues to the words. Write the words on the lines.

 ngruspnewialu

 micalendstlilw

 vocglossesk

 oteoschclsetewa

262 Jungly wordsearch

Look in the wordsearch grid for eight jungle creatures.
You will find them by reading across or down.
Draw a ring around the words as you find them.

A	U	X	Q	D	P	C	Q	P
Y	X	M	S	N	A	K	E	K
F	R	O	G	G	R	H	B	T
V	R	N	J	W	R	Z	Y	O
V	Y	K	G	T	O	L	Q	U
Y	E	E	R	G	T	I	U	C
U	A	Y	D	H	J	Z	B	A
S	P	I	D	E	R	A	V	N
Y	B	X	Y	F	E	R	H	U
L	E	O	P	A	R	D	H	K

263 Cheese hunt

Help the mice through the maze to the cheese by following
the numbers in the eight times table.

264 At the station

Look carefully at these two pictures.
There are 10 differences. Can you spot them?

265 A lot of legs crossword

The pictures of creatures with lots of legs are clues to the words.
Follow the numbers across and down, and write the words in the grid.

266 Tarzan's troubles

Help Tarzan to find his way through the maze back to his tree house.

267 Out to pasture

Follow the lines to see which flower each cow has.

268 Odd one out

Look at each row of objects.
Put a tick next to the picture that is the odd one out in each row.

269 Missing middles

These words are missing their middle letters.
Complete the words using the pictures as clues.

ca _ _ le

mo _ _ ey

jo _ _ ey

do _ _ ey

270 Clothes code

Use the code to work out the answers to the sums.

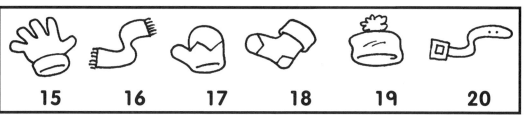

15	16	17	18	19	20

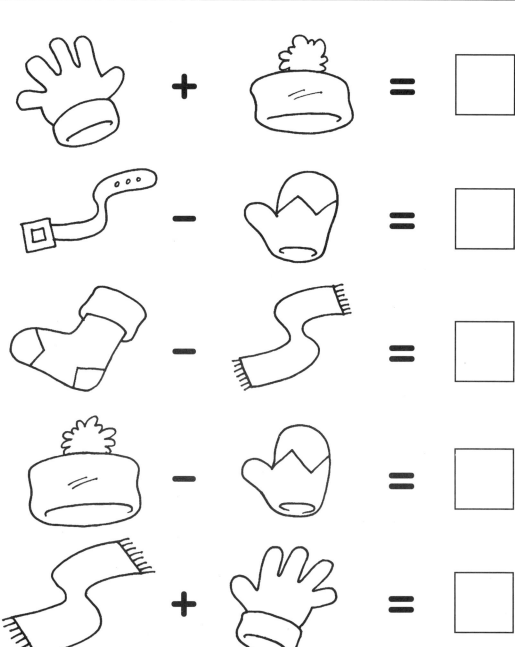

271 First past the post

Look at the symbols in the box. Each symbol represents a different number of minutes. Add up the times to see which horse finishes first.

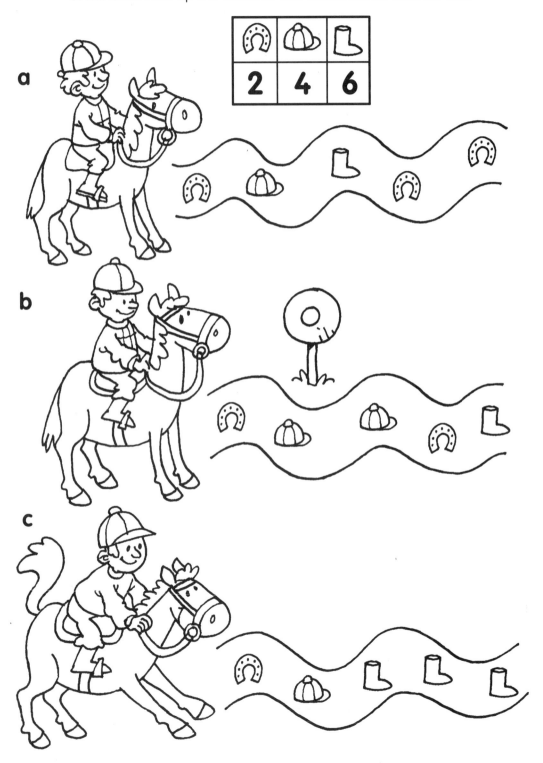

272 Adding-up bananas

Count how many bananas each gorilla has and write
the numbers in the boxes. Then do the sum.

☐ + ☐ + ☐ + ☐ + ☐

= ☐ bananas
altogether

273 **Sums puzzles**

Do the sums in the grids by filling in the missing numbers and symbols.

274 Picture wheel

Write the first letter of each picture in the space in the centre of the picture wheel. You will spell the name of a scaly creature.

275 Rhyming words

Draw lines to join the words that rhyme.

fish

socks

boat

rain

fox

dish

train

goat

276 **Jungle fever**

Starting with number 1, draw a line to join the dots
and complete the picture.

277 Number patterns

Look at the numbers in the lily pads and write
in the missing numbers.

278 Creepy caterpillars

Do the multiplication sums in these caterpillars.

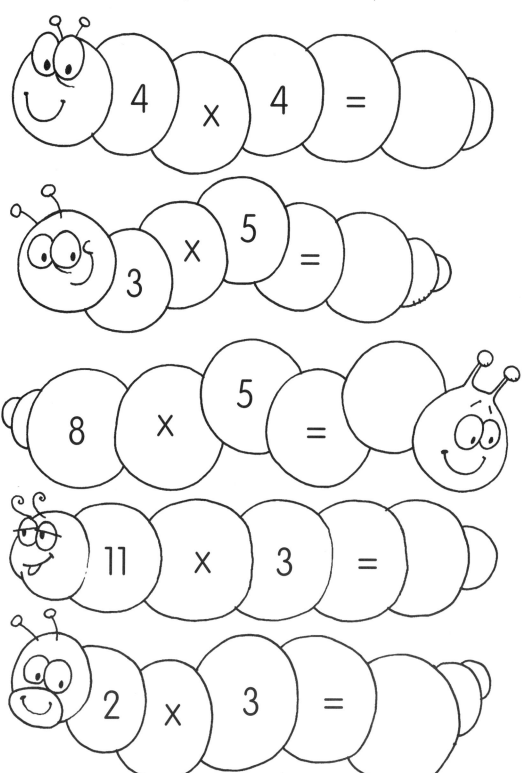

$4 \times 4 =$

$3 \times 5 =$

$8 \times 5 =$

$11 \times 3 =$

$2 \times 3 =$

279 Heads and tails

Write the first letter of each picture in the boxes.
You will make a new word.

☐ r o k e ☐

☐ h o u l ☐

☐ e t a i ☐

☐ o u n c ☐

280 Puppy shadow

Can you match the boy and his puppy with their shadow?

281 Toadstool sums

Do these subtraction sums.
Join the sums to the answers.

10

9

5

2

18 - 9

13 - 3

17 - 12

9 - 7

282 What is it?

Starting with the letter 'k', cross out every other letter to spell a word.
Write the word on the line.

kcgruoyciopdwixlcev

_____

283 Little Miss Muffet

Look at the pictures and work out the correct order of this story.
Write the numbers 1 to 4 in the boxes.

284 **Word trail**

Use the picture clues to fill in the word trail. The last letter of each word
is the first letter of the next word.

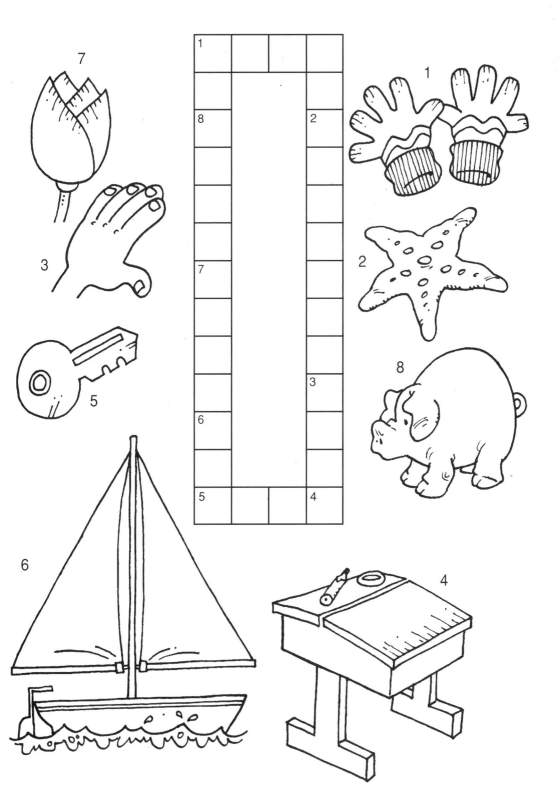

285 New words

How many new words can you make from the word 'paintbrush'?
Write the new words on the paint pot.

paintbrush

286 Letter codes

Using the code in the box as a guide, fill in the missing letters
to spell a fruit.

	1	2	3	4	5	6
A	m	l	k	n	h	l
B	i	t	n	t	e	e
C	u	z	a	p	o	p
D	w	e	b	p	y	r
E	a	e	c	f	b	n
F	a	s	p	p	t	y

___ ___ ___ ___ ___ ___ ___ ___
F3   B1   B3   B5   F1   D4   C6   A6   E2

287 Hidden words

In each grid, cross out the letters that appear more than once to discover the hidden words. Write the words on the lines.

m	o	a	i	n
h	r	l	b	d
t	y	s	o	h
r	b	e	m	l
s	i	d	n	y

_____

d	f	c	i	o
p	i	g	l	d
a	h	k	p	r
r	e	u	f	l
u	o	g	s	h

_____

288 Dividing

Do these division sums and draw lines to match the answers
with the correct group below.

$$48 \div 12 = \boxed{4}$$

$$5 \div 5 = \boxed{1}$$

$$30 \div 10 = \boxed{3}$$

$$63 \div 9 = \boxed{7}$$

289 Time for take-off

Look carefully at these two pictures.
There are eight differences. Can you spot them?

290 Wizardly ways

Help the wizard to find his crystal ball by following the numbers
in the nine times table.

291 Space wordsearch

Look in the wordsearch grid for _eight_ things you might see in space.
You will find them by reading across or down.
Draw a ring around the words as you find them.

```
S  Y  A  Q  T  Y  W  N  A
A  B  X  R  J  G  R  Q  L
T  S  U  N  T  Y  O  U  I
E  T  A  Q  F  O  C  P  E
L  A  F  V  Z  S  K  R  N
L  R  P  L  A  N  E  T  H
I  S  P  E  Y  T  T  R  V
T  M  O  O  N  B  M  N  U
E  H  B  Y  Q  V  R  W  Q
T  Y  R  B  C  O  M  E  T
```

292 Word scrambles

There are two words hidden in each row of scrambled letters.
The pictures are clues to the words. Write the words on the lines.

tlbaow

owl   owl

bat

choanoatrb

boat

anchor

rdamyicmelpa

camel

pyramid

etanrloketpc

rocket

planet

293 Counting under the sea

Look carefully at this picture. How many different things can you count?
Write the answers in the boxes.

octopuses	lobsters	shells	fish	bubbles
3	5	10	14	14

294 **Party code**

Use the code to work out the answers to the sums.

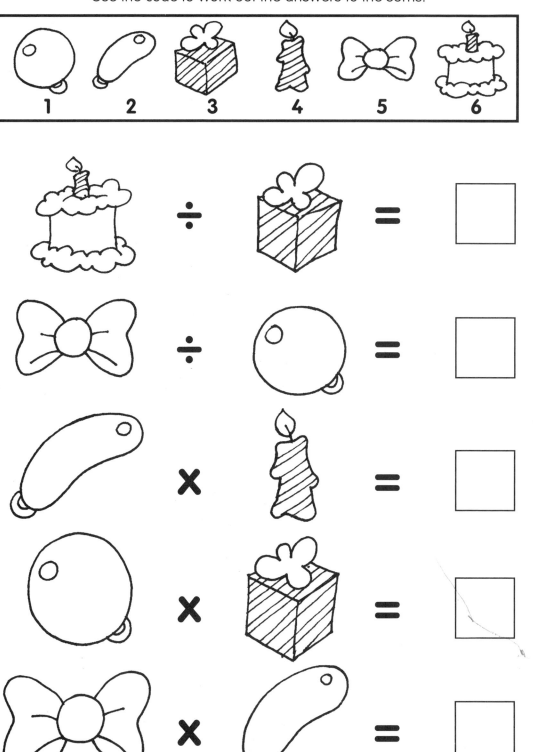

295 Missing letters

These words are missing some letters.
Complete the words using the pictures as clues.

_ _oves

_ _land

_ _oud

_ _agon

296 Odd one out

Look at each row of objects.
Put a tick next to the picture that is the odd one out in each row.

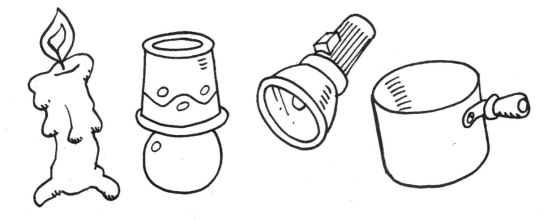

297 On your marks

Follow the lines to see which horse each jockey is going to ride.

298 Pyramid problems

Help the Pharaoh to get through the maze to the pyramid.

299 Buildings crossword

The pictures of buildings are clues to the words. Follow the numbers across and down, and write the words in the grid.

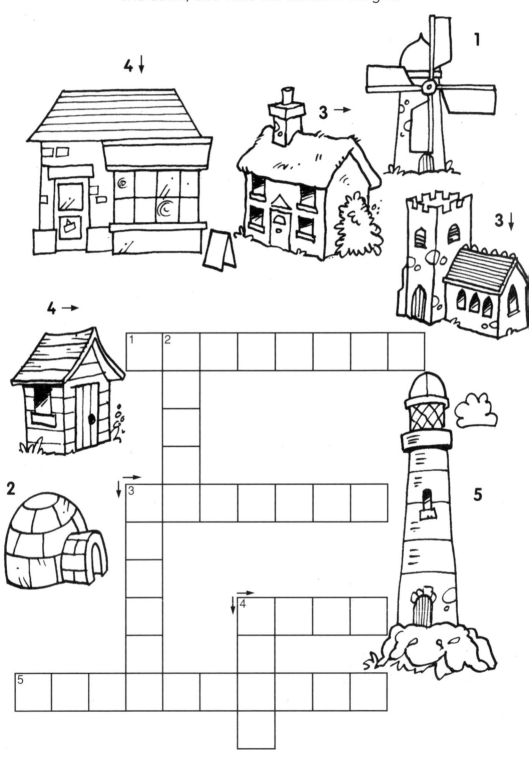

300 Number patterns

Look at the numbers in the flowers and write
in the missing numbers.

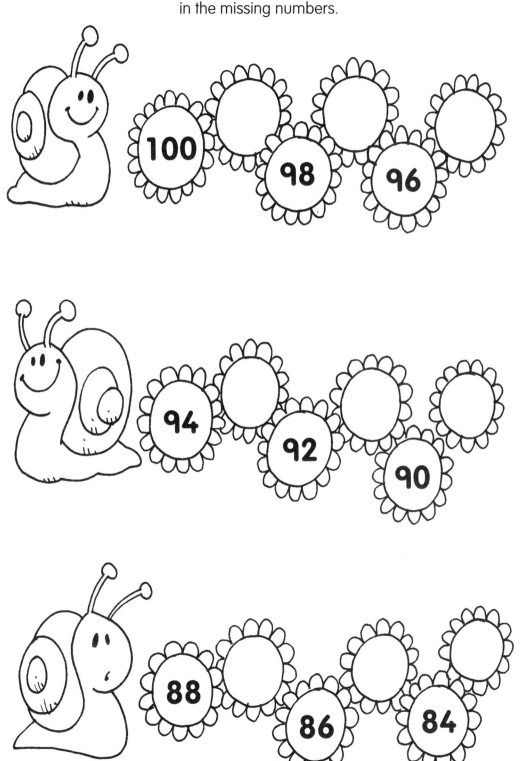

301 **Touch down**

Starting with number 1, draw a line to join the dots and
complete the picture.

302 **Rhyming words**
Draw lines to join the words that rhyme.

mouse

rat

toy

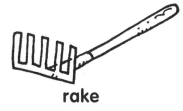

rake

bat

house

snake

boy

303 Picture wheel

Write the first letter of each picture in the space in the centre of the picture wheel. You will spell the name of a mechanical friend.

304 Sums puzzles

Do the sums in the grids by filling in the missing numbers.

	×	2	=	6
+	■	−	■	−
1	×		=	
=	■	=	■	=
4	+		=	5

4	+		=	6
×	■	−	■	+
	+	1	=	
=	■	=	■	=
8	+	1	=	

305 Adding-up holes

Count the holes in each cheese and write
the numbers in the boxes. Then do the sum.

□ + □ + □ + □ + □

= □ holes
altogether

306 Snail's pace

Look at the symbols in the box. Each symbol represents a different number of minutes. Add up the times to see which snail is slowest.

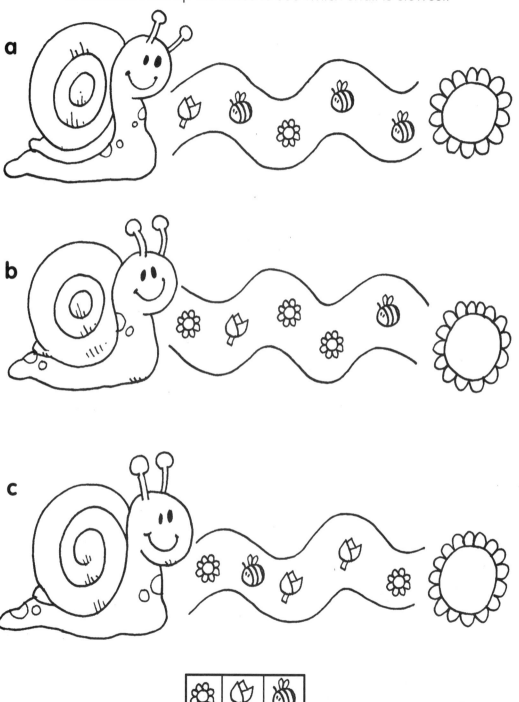

307 Crocodile sums

Do these subtraction sums.
Join the sums to the answers.

0

14 - 7

6

8 - 2

1

10 - 10

7

20 - 19

308 Ape shape

Can you match the ape with its shadow?

309 Heads and tails

Write the first letter of each picture in the boxes.
You will make a new word.

☐ t r e a ☐

☐ r o z e ☐

☐ l a c e ☐

☐ u m p e ☐

310 Multiplying ladders

Do the multiplication sums in these ladders.

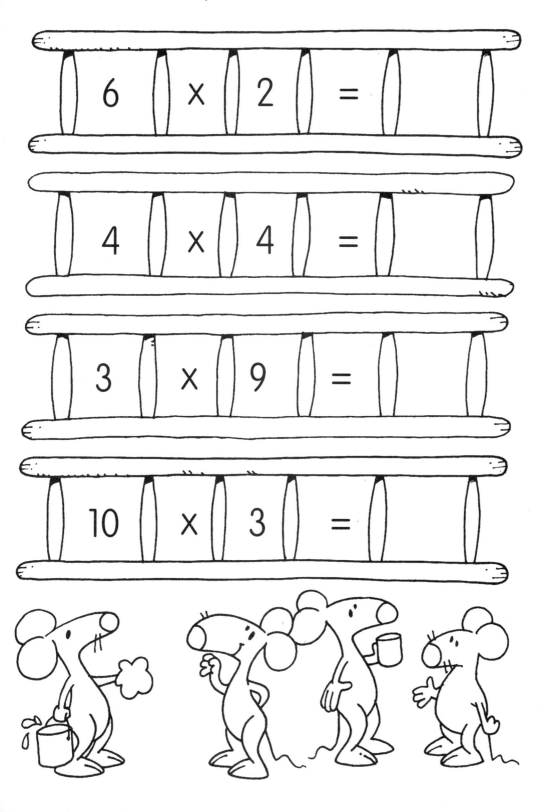

6 × 2 =

4 × 4 =

3 × 9 =

10 × 3 =

311 Letter codes

Using the code in the box as a guide, fill in the missing letters to spell something festive.

	1	2	3	4	5	6
A	t	n	a	u	p	a
B	k	i	t	u	o	e
C	u	s	b	i	n	v
D	o	r	x	c	z	r
E	w	l	o	f	y	p
F	w	s	n	m	e	a

___ ___ ___ ___ ___ ___ ___
C2 A2 E3 F1 F4 A6 C5

312 New words

How many new words can you make from the word 'spaceship'?
Write the new words in the alien's spaceship.

spaceship

313 **Word trail**

Use the picture clues to fill in the word trail. The last letter of each word is the first letter of the next word.

314 **Going camping**

Look at the pictures and work out the correct order of this story.
Write the numbers 1 to 4 in the boxes.

Starting with the letter 'd', cross out every other letter to spell a word.
Write the word on the line.

dsftgrbanwkboeirtrxya

_____

316 Hidden words

In each grid, cross out the letters that appear more than once to discover the hidden words. Write the words on the lines.

h	i	p	u	z
g	r	h	m	d
d	p	o	i	n
a	z	u	r	l
b	m	s	n	b

_____

e	m	r	o	i
l	d	a	y	v
t	v	o	e	g
y	r	d	c	l
e	h	g	i	e

_____

317 Dividing

Do these division sums and draw lines to match the answers with the correct group below.

$$7 \div 7 = \boxed{}$$

$$16 \div 4 = \boxed{}$$

$$27 \div 9 = \boxed{}$$

$$16 \div 2 = \boxed{}$$

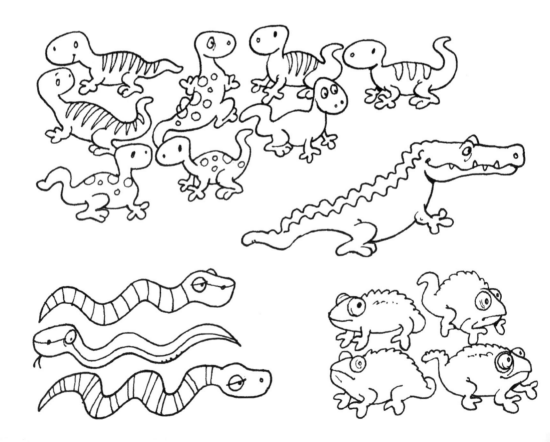

318 Counting bugs

Look carefully at this picture. How many different things can you count?
Write the answers in the boxes.

spiders	toadstools	caterpillars	ladybird spots	ants

319 Word scrambles

There are two words hidden in each row of scrambled letters.
The pictures are clues to the words. Write the words on the lines.

wsduaknc

_____

_____

atkcwlochc

_____

_____

pultobsocserto

_____

_____

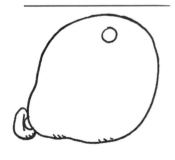

relbntalopsone

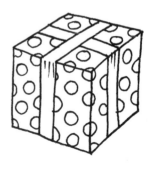

_____

320 Festive fun wordsearch

Look in the wordsearch grid for eight Christmas-time things.
You will find them by reading across or down.
Draw a ring around the words as you find them.

R	X	A	N	G	E	L	I	B
E	B	Q	F	B	S	T	P	J
I	E	U	E	G	T	H	R	K
N	L	H	X	C	A	K	E	L
D	L	H	W	R	R	X	S	Z
E	C	W	B	T	Y	H	E	G
E	H	O	L	L	Y	M	N	R
R	V	D	E	U	J	N	T	Y
Q	F	H	J	Q	W	K	S	U
X	S	N	O	W	M	A	N	B

321 Lost in space

Help the alien to find his way back to the Moon by following the numbers that can be divided exactly by 12.

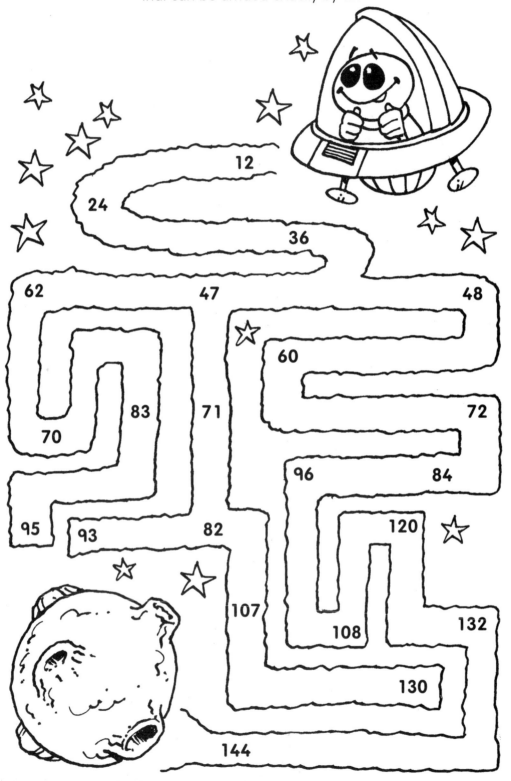

322 Splish, splash

Look carefully at these two pictures.
There are seven differences. Can you spot them?

323 **Christmas code**

Use the code to work out the answers to the sums.

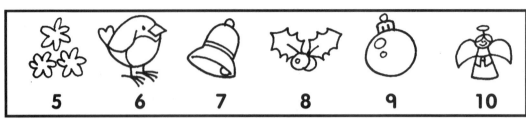

❄	🐦	🔔	🍃	⚪	👼
5	6	7	8	9	10

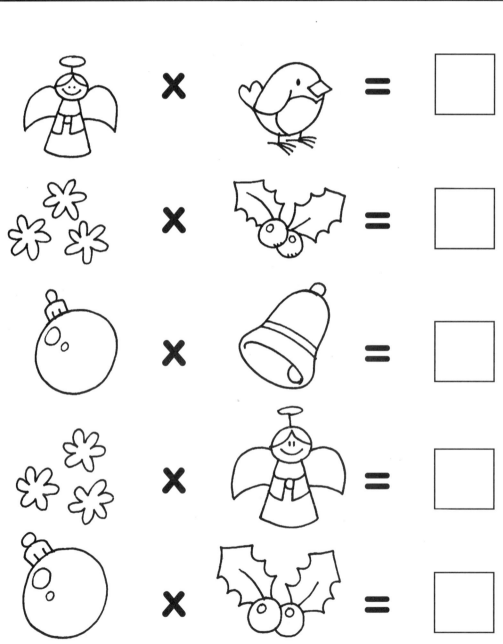

324 Missing letters
These words are missing some letters.
Complete the words using the pictures as clues.

_ _ _ e

_ _ _ en

_ _ _ tar

_ _ _ nge

325 Odd one out

Look at each row of objects.
Put a tick next to the picture that is the odd one out in each row.

326 Which cat?

Follow the lines to join the cats with their witchy owners.

327 Going to school

Help the children to get through the maze to their school.

328 Ready, steady, go crossword

The numbers on the children's t-shirts are clues to the words.
Write the words in the grid.

329 Number patterns

Look at the numbers in the kites and write in the missing numbers.

330 **Flutter by**

Starting with number 10, draw a line to join the dots
and complete the picture.

331 Sounds the same

The letters 'ee' and 'ea' sometimes make the same sound.
Add 'ee' or 'ea' to complete these words.

f_ _t

b_ _

sw_ _ts

l_ _f

tr_ _

s_ _t

b_ _ver

s_ _l

332 Picture wheel

Write the first letter of each picture in the space in the centre of the picture wheel. You will spell the name of something with three wheels.

333 Sums puzzle

Do the sums in the grid by filling in the missing numbers and symbol.

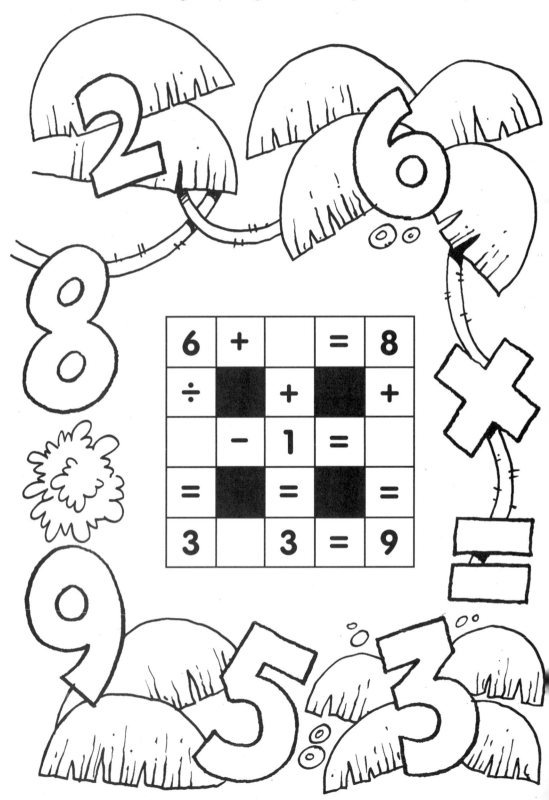

6	+		=	8
÷	■	+	■	+
	−	1	=	
=	■	=	■	=
3		3	=	9

334 Adding-up balls

Count how many juggling balls each clown has and write
the numbers in the boxes. Then do the sum.

☐ + ☐ + ☐ + ☐ + ☐

= ☐ **balls
altogether**

335 Mole madness

Look at the symbols in the box. Each symbol represents a different number of minutes. Add up the times to see which mole reaches its burrow first.

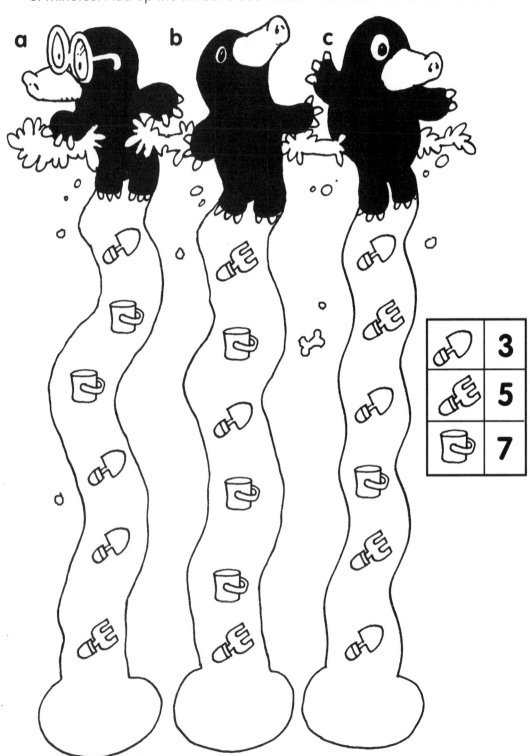

336 Beehive sums

Do these subtraction sums.
Join the sums to the answers.

8

2

14

3

6 - 4

17 - 9

9 - 6

19 - 5

337 Fairy shadow

Can you match the fairy with her shadow?

338 Heads and tails

Write the first letter of each picture in the boxes.
You will make a new word.

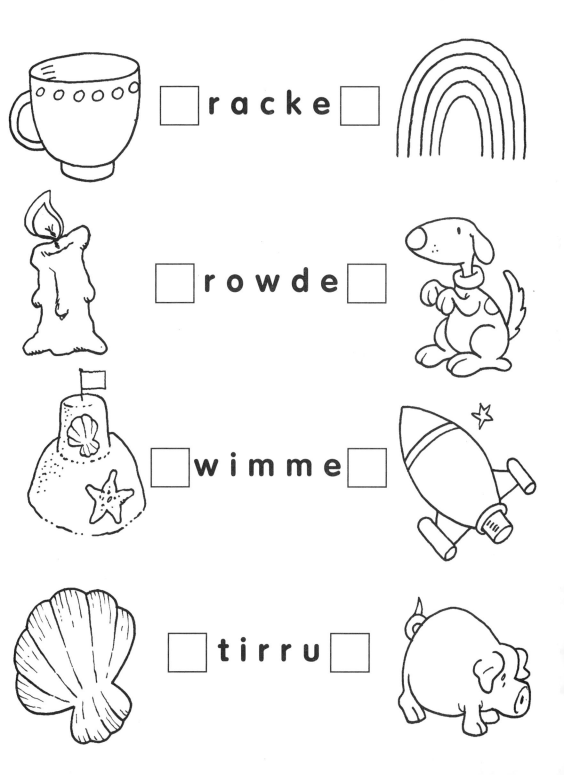

☐ r a c k e ☐

☐ r o w d e ☐

☐ w i m m e ☐

☐ t i r r u ☐

339 Beetle sums

Do the multiplication sums in these beetles.

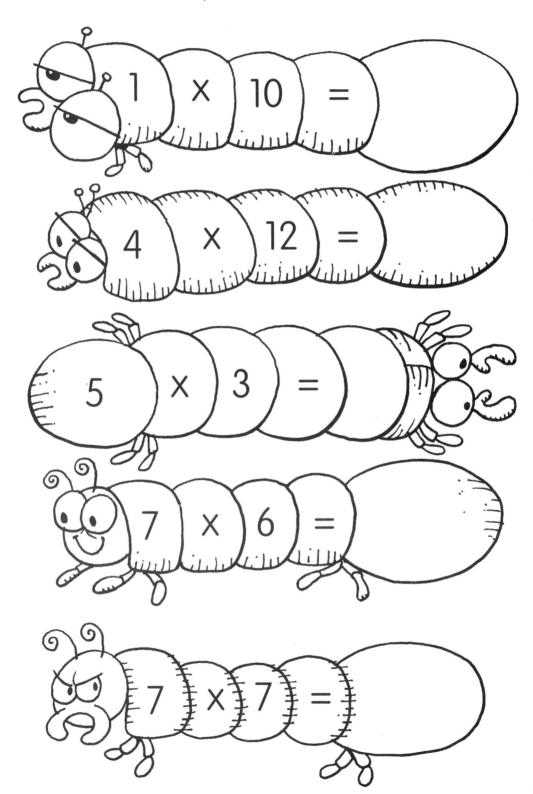

1 × 10 =

4 × 12 =

5 × 3 =

7 × 6 =

7 × 7 =

340 Dividing

Do these division sums and draw lines to match the answers
with the correct group below.

$$48 \div 8 = \boxed{}$$

$$20 \div 4 = \boxed{}$$

$$144 \div 12 = \boxed{}$$

$$20 \div 2 = \boxed{}$$

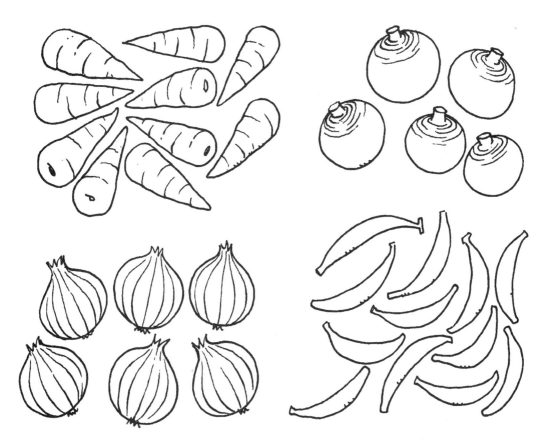

341 Hidden words

In each grid, cross out the letters that appear more than once to discover the hidden words. Write the words on the lines.

p	o	i	h	g
w	m	g	n	b
f	i	a	p	z
b	t	f	h	n
z	o	e	m	r

water

w	a	s	f	t
n	u	i	g	o
b	t	r	h	w
a	k	u	f	e
i	g	l	b	h

snorkel

342 **What is it?**

Starting with the letter 'q', cross out every other letter to spell a word.
Write the word on the line.

qhgemlbikcioopptvedri

_____

343 Counting at a party

Look carefully at this picture. How many different things can you count?
Write the answers in the boxes.

hats	candles	cakes	balloons	presents

344 Word scrambles

There are two words hidden in each row of scrambled letters.
The pictures are clues to the words. Write the words on the lines.

osrnourcted

_____   _____

atcryiwihf

_____   _____

taonrsmos

_____   _____

ghraeantelepfif

_____   _____

345 Spooky wordsearch

Look in the wordsearch grid for eight spooky things.
You will find them by reading across or down.
Draw a ring around the words as you find them.

V	A	M	P	I	R	E	Z	X
X	N	V	G	W	Q	S	Z	H
Y	W	U	H	I	Q	V	B	F
A	I	S	O	Z	X	F	A	T
G	T	D	S	G	Y	B	T	S
U	C	A	T	V	R	Y	U	P
C	H	Q	T	Y	U	I	O	I
C	P	U	M	P	K	I	N	D
Y	A	C	B	N	M	H	I	E
X	G	M	O	N	S	T	E	R

346 All aboard!

Help the travellers to find their train by following the numbers in the 11 times table.

347 **Playtime**

Look carefully at these two pictures.
There are eight differences. Can you spot them?

348 Happy holiday crossword

The pictures of holiday things are clues to the words.
Follow the numbers across and down, and write the words in the grid.

3 →

3 ↓

1

2

5

7

6

349 Mister Mole

Help the mole to find his way through the maze back to his burrow.

350 Whose shoes?

Follow the tangled laces to see who owns each pair of shoes.

351 **Odd one out**

Look at each row of objects.
Put a tick next to the picture that is the odd one out in each row.

352 Plural endings

Change these words from singular spellings to plural spellings.
Write the words on the lines.

mushroom

_____

witch

_____

fairy

_____

pumpkin

_____

353 Halloween code

Use the code to work out the answers to the sums.

15	16	17	18	19	20

354 Hopping about

Look at the symbols in the box. Each symbol represents a different number of minutes. Add up the times to see which kangaroo wins the race.

355 Adding-up eggs

Count the eggs in each nest and write
the numbers in the boxes. Then do the sum.

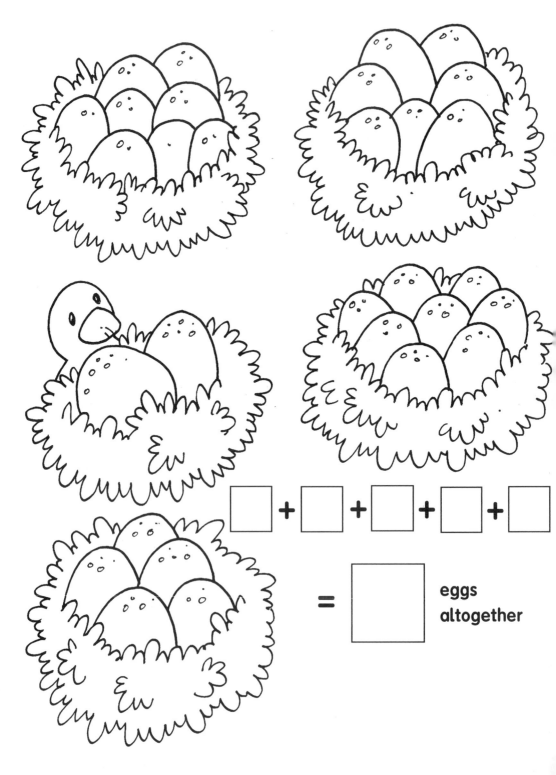

☐ + ☐ + ☐ + ☐ + ☐

= ☐ eggs
altogether

356 Sums puzzle

Do the sums in the grid by filling in the missing numbers.

4	+	12	=	16
+		+		−
14	−	2	=	12
=		=		=
18	−	14	=	4

357 Picture wheel

Write the first letter of each picture in the space in the centre of the picture wheel. You will spell the name of a furry friend.

358 Number patterns

Look at the numbers in the sails and write
in the missing numbers.

359 Clowning around

Starting with number 100, draw a line to join the dots and complete the picture.

360 Sounds the same

The letters 'ou' and 'ow' sometimes make the same sound.
Add 'ou' or 'ow' to complete these words.

cl _ _ d

fl _ _ er

tr _ _ el

c _ _

r _ _ ndab _ _ t

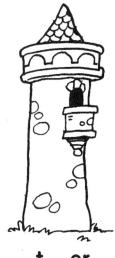

t _ _ er

l _ _ d

fl _ _ r

361 Give the dog a bone sums

Do these subtraction sums.
Join the sums to the answers.

5

10

4

7

16 - 6

12 - 7

7 - 3

20 - 13

362 Wiggly-worm sums

Do the multiplication sums in these wiggly worms.

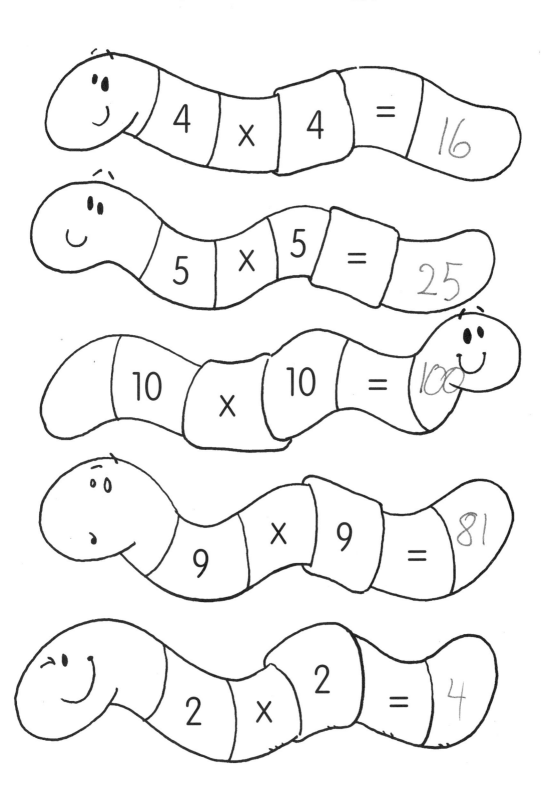

$4 \times 4 = 16$

$5 \times 5 = 25$

$10 \times 10 = 100$

$9 \times 9 = 81$

$2 \times 2 = 4$

363 Hidden words

In each grid, cross out the letters that appear more than once to discover the hidden words. Write the words on the lines.

k	t	l	n	d
c	z	i	o	b
n	l	d	m	w
b	c	z	o	h
h	e	w	k	b

_____

w	s	r	d	e
a	n	t	g	m
m	e	x	v	p
g	c	n	r	x
s	v	h	d	p

_____

364 Dividing

Do these division sums and draw lines to match the answers
with the correct group below.

$$8 \div 4 = \boxed{}$$

$$28 \div 7 = \boxed{}$$

$$36 \div 4 = \boxed{}$$

$$32 \div 2 = \boxed{}$$

365 Slippery slope

Help the skier down the mountain by following the EVEN numbers.

Answers

2 Word scrambles
scooter doll pear cherry
butterfly spider violin trumpet

3 Spooky spellings
dragon witch wizard
ghost pumpkin castle

4 Things that go wordsearch

6 Garden games
1. girl's pocket
2. girl's shoe
3. bush missing a flower
4. toadstool missing spots
5. water drop missing
6. boy holding different flower
7. boy's stripe on t-shirt
8. boy's trowel
9. boy's pockets on trousers
10. mud on spade

7 On safari
giraffe elephant gorilla zebra

10 Missing middles
rocket jacket anchor basket

15 Animal magic crossword

(crossword grid)

16 Beginning with 's'
sign, skirt, shelf, scarf, sausages, shirt, sleeves, sock, spectacles, sweets, socks, shoes, sandwich, scales, straws... can you think of any more?

20 Picture wheel
apple

21 Sums puzzles

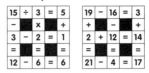

15	÷	3	=	5
−		×		+
3	−	2	=	1
=		=		=
12	−	6	=	6

19	−	16	=	3
+		−		+
2	+	12	=	14
=		=		=
21	−	4	=	17

22 Weather scramble
rainbow umbrella raincoat
boots hat clouds

23 Addition
$1 + 2 = 3$ $4 + 2 = 6$
$2 + 6 = 8$ $6 + 6 = 12$

25 Size wise
Sid is 5 cm long.   Molly is 9 cm long.
Molly is longer than Sid.
Sid is shorter than Molly.

26 Make it plural
cars watches apples dishes trees

28 Funny farm
1. flying fish
2. water coming out of chimney
3. cow with antlers
4. dinosaur
5. boy wearing rubber ring
6. farmer hoovering outside
7. farmer wearing a slipper
8. hen with three legs

30 Heads and tails
log bad cat zip

32 Trivia
b. John Logie Baird

33 Trivia
c. Italy

34 Adding 'e'
use cane care pine

35 Letter codes
giraffe

37 Word trail
1. rocket 2. toad 3. daffodil 4. leopard
5. deckchair 6. reindeer

39 What is it?
penguin

40 Weather code
5 + 3 = 8   6 + 1 = 7   2 + 4 = 6
3 + 6 = 9   1 + 2 = 3

42 Playtime problems
1. aeroplane upside-down
2. boys throwing cake
3. fish in tree
4. boy with bird's feet
5. man dressed as Father Christmas
6. girl with wings
7. girl riding turtle
8. boy holding light bulb

44 Heads and tails
cow toy bee fin

46 What is it?
ladybird

48 Word trail
1. rhinoceros 2. ski 3. igloo 4. onion 5. net
6. turtle 7. elephant 8. tent 9. tractor

50 Letter codes
bicycle

51 Adding 'e'
one cape pipe here

52 Trivia
b. a herd

53 Trivia
b. a spectre

54 Subtraction sums
6 - 3 = 3   5 - 1 = 4   10 - 7 = 3

55 Hidden words
magic wand

56 Garden code
6 x 2 = 12   3 x 1 = 3   4 x 5 = 20
2 x 1 = 2   6 x 4 = 24

58 Dividing
10 ÷ 2 = 5   12 ÷ 3 = 4
15 ÷ 5 = 3   18 ÷ 3 = 6

60 Word scrambles
lion tiger table chair
book pencil skirt dress

61 Animal spellings
giraffe kangaroo koala
gorilla tiger zebra

62 Under the sea wordsearch

63 The fair's in town
1. boy's smile
2. girl's dungarees pocket
3. girl's dungarees button missing
4. pattern on roof of carousel
5. man's hat band
6. man's waistcoat pocket
7. missing coconut
8. girl's dungarees knee patch
9. spots on man's bow tie
10. man's shoe

64 Walkabout
LONDON DUBLIN CARDIFF EDINBURGH

66 Pyramid problem
14 triangles

67 Flower power crossword

72 Missing middles
ladder parrot rabbit bottle

73 Seaside code
10 + 7 = 17   8 + 9 = 17   6 + 5 = 11
7 + 8 = 15   9 + 5 = 14

76 Addition
1 + 1 = 2   4 + 4 = 8   8 + 2 = 10   9 + 3 = 12

77 Mini-beast scramble
butterfly worm ladybird
beetle ant caterpillar

78 Sums puzzles

3	+	9	=	12		7	+	4	=	11
×		×		÷		×		−		+
12	÷	2	=	6		3	×	3	=	9
=		=		=		=		=		=
36	÷	18	=	2		21	−	1	=	20

79 Picture wheel
magician

83 Wiggly worms
Wally is 10 cm long.   Wendy is 7 cm long.

84 Make it plural
foxes boats sandwiches gloves brushes

85 Subtraction sums
13 - 8 = 5   11 - 5 = 6   9 - 6 = 3

87 Football crazy
1. goalie wearing a skirt
2. gorilla on team
3. boy wearing tie
4. boy carrying tennis racket
5. boy wearing mask
6. boy carrying sausages
7. rugby ball instead of football
8. crab on pitch

89 Heads and tails
soon good leap trip

91 Dinosaur sums
5 x 5 = 25   9 x 9 = 81   4 x 6 = 24

92 Trivia
a. a mammal

93 Trivia
c. 0°C

94 Adding a letter
cart camp card crow

95 Letter codes
butterfly

97 Word trail
1. walrus 2. skull 3. lizard 4. dandelion
5. necklace 6. elephant 7. tie 8. elbow

99 What is it?
windmill

100 Hidden words
cloud storm

102 Dividing
12 ÷ 1 = 12   24 ÷ 12 = 2
48 ÷ 6 = 8   49 ÷ 7 = 7

104 Word scrambles
snail flower farmer tractor
sandals shoes wand wizard

105 Sea spellings
whale shells lobster
dolphin crab fish

106 Girls' names wordsearch

W	M	D	F	S	U	B	B	X
S	A	R	A	H	G	P	E	O
V	R	F	O	A	B	N	C	U
N	I	Z	Y	R	R	C	K	W
X	A	J	T	O	V	A	Y	U
Q	F	C	G	N	A	N	C	G
J	B	T	G	W	E	N	O	X
L	O	R	N	A	H	E	Q	T
T	U	H	D	Z	Y	J	H	V
W	E	X	Z	N	I	C	K	Y

108 Fun on the farm
1. pig's tail missing
2. farmer's scarf
3. food in trough
4. farmer's boot
5. missing brick in wall
6. hay on fork
7. farmer's buckle

109 Fairground fun
big wheel helter-skelter
bumper cars merry-go-round

111 Crossword of colours

				G		
		O	R	E	D	
P	U	R	P	L	E	
I		A		E		
N		N		N		
K		G				
Y	E	L	L	O	W	
				H		
				I		
				T		
B	L	U	E			

116 Missing middles
puppet carrot pillow kettle

117 Fruity code
10 + 12 = 22   14 - 11 = 3   13 + 15 = 28
12 + 14 = 26   15 - 11 = 4

119 Addition
$1 + 1 = 2$ $2 + 5 = 7$
$7 + 2 = 9$ $8 + 3 = 11$

120 Clothing scramble
dress trousers shirt
shoes socks   skirt

121 Sums puzzles

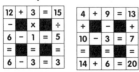

12	+	3	=	15
−	×			÷
6	−	1	=	5
=		=		=
6	−	3	=	3

4	+	9	=	13
+		−		+
10	−	3	=	7
=		=		=
14	+	6	=	20

122 Picture wheel
mouse

123 Longer words
honeymoon toothbrush
staircase   gooseberries

126 Spotty-cow sums
$3 \times 5 = 15$ $6 \times 6 = 36$ $2 \times 8 = 16$

128 Heads and tails
fear main stew eggs

130 Party madness
1, raining upwards
2. clock numbers wrong
3. plant balloon
4. dog in clothes
5. boy with scuba tank
6. boy wearing fish tie
7. boy with three arms
8. boy on skis

132 Subtraction sums
$6 - 3 = 3$ $12 - 5 = 7$ $10 - 3 = 7$

133 Plural endings
feet mice spies geese scarves

134 What is it?
snowflake

136 Word trail
1. shell 2. leopard 3. drum 4. mermaid
5. diamond 6. doctor 7. rose 8. egg
9. goat 10. toads

138 Letter codes
octopus

139 Adding a letter
blend bomb brand blind

140 Trivia
a. a carnivore

141 Trivia
a. a book of words

142 Dividing
$12 \div 3 = 4$ $25 \div 5 = 5$
$81 \div 9 = 9$ $100 \div 10 = 10$

144 Hidden words
NICKY LINDA

146 Word scrambles
knight princess   apple banana
horse rabbit   boat canoe

147 Shape spellings
square   circle triangle
rectangle oval   cube

148 Mini beasts wordsearch

150 Ball skills
1. tree
2. girl's hat
3. girl's eyebrow
4. pattern on ball
5. flower missing on boy's shirt
6. worm
7. stripe on girl's shorts
8. dog's mouth
9. patch on dog
10. dog's collar

151 At the airport
CANADA   AUSTRALIA NEW ZEALAND
CHINA   INDIA   MEXICO   JAPAN

153 Yummy crossword

158 Missing letters
squid strawberry squirrel skates

159 Flower sums
$7 \times 7 = 49$ $8 \times 6 = 48$ $7 \times 9 = 63$

161 Addition
$3 + 2 = 5$ $1 + 5 = 6$
$7 + 3 = 10$ $10 + 4 = 14$

162 Pond-life scramble
duckling frog flowers bridge swan goose

163 Sums puzzles

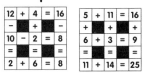

164 Picture wheel
dolphins

165 Longer words
football drumstick horseshoe earwig

168 A lot of legs sums
$8 \times 8 = 64$ $4 \times 6 = 24$ $8 \times 4 = 32$

170 Heads and tails
rain cake bell cook

172 Crazy camping
1. lollipop tree
2. flower pot on boy's head
3. man with wheel for legs
4. tea pouring upwards
5. moon and sun
6. penguin in tent
7. girl playing with octopus
8. chimney on tent

174 Subtraction sums
$14 - 7 = 7$ $4 - 2 = 2$ $7 - 1 = 6$

175 Make it plural
boxes tigers potatoes scarecrows buses

176 What is it?
motorbike

178 Word trail
1. king 2. ghost 3. trumpet 4. teeth
5. holly 6. yo-yo 7. octopus 8. star
9. rabbits 10. sink

180 Letter codes
castle

181 Taking away 'e'
to rip hat win

182 Trivia
a. a dodo

183 Trivia
b. a joey

184 Dividing
$32 \div 4 = 8$ $56 \div 8 = 7$
$33 \div 11 = 3$ $30 \div 2 = 15$

185 Tell the time
a. 3:00 b. 1:30 c. 11:15 d. 4:45 e. 7:30

186 Hidden names
SIMON NIGEL

188 Word scrambles
mouse cheese   robin parrot
crab   shark   tulip daisy

189 Pet spellings
goldfish hamster parrot
horse   rabbit   puppy

190 Boys' names wordsearch

192 Race to the finish
1. last boy's mouth
2. number on t-shirt
3. second boy's hair
4. second boy's number
5. second boy's shorts
6. second boy's trainers
7. clump of grass
8. tree
9. first boy's hair
10. first boy's t-shirt

193 Seeing sights
museum art gallery castle statue

195 Ball code
$10 - 8 = 2$ $5 + 7 = 12$ $6 + 10 = 16$
$7 + 8 = 15$ $9 - 6 = 3$

196 Missing letters
grapes plum clown drink

201 Up a tree crossword

204 Outer space
padlock bookshelf bedroom fairground

205 Picture wheel
carrot

206 Sums puzzles
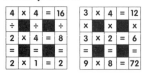

207 Addition
$2 + 3 = 5$ $1 + 8 = 9$
$4 + 6 = 10$ $7 + 4 = 11$

209 Make it plural
sandcastles bushes candles
glasses   elephants

210 Subtraction sums
$9 - 5 = 4$ $15 - 5 = 10$ $11 - 9 = 2$

211 Clown shadow
d. is the shadow

212 Heads and tails
tulip heart cheap order

213 T-shirt sums
$2 \times 5 = 10$ $6 \times 10 = 60$ $11 \times 7 = 77$

214 Trivia
b. a calf

215 Trivia
b. a gaggle

216 Letter codes
tractor

218 Word trail
1. towel 2. lamp 3. panda 4. apple
5. earwig 6. gate 7. ear 8. root

220 What is it?
hamster

222 Word trail
1. watch 2. hat 3. table 4. emu 5. umbrella
6. ant 7. trucks 8. saw

224 Letter codes
wizard

225 Hidden words
owl bat

226 Tell the time
a. 4:00 b. 1:45 c. 10:30 d. 7:15 e. 9:00

227 Dividing
$36 \div 6 = 6$ $45 \div 5 = 9$
$24 \div 8 = 3$ $12 \div 12 = 1$

228 Trivia
a. Thomas Edison

229 Trivia
b. thatched

231 Word scrambles
clown astronaut robot television
snake panda bowl plate

232 Lunch-box spellings
cake sandwich orange
chocolate apple crisps

233 Sporty wordsearch

235 Gone fishing
1. sun missing
2. band on man's hat
3. button on man's collar
4. man's mug
5. patch on man's trousers
6. boy's net
7. stripes on boy's t-shirt
8. flower missing
9. boy's sandal
10. handle on reel

236 Treasure island crossword

240 Missing letters
sink teeth candle cactus

241 Footwear code
$10 + 11 = 21$ $12 + 15 = 27$ $13 + 14 = 27$
$10 + 12 = 22$ $11 + 15 = 26$

243 Adding-up spines
$1 + 6 + 3 + 4 + 3 = 17$

244 Sums puzzles
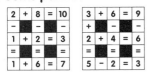

245 Picture wheel
flower

246 Oranges and lemons
fingerprint carpet goldfish necklace

249 Sum snakes
$7 \times 7 = 49$ $6 \times 8 = 48$ $10 \times 9 = 90$
$9 \times 6 = 54$ $12 \times 2 = 24$

250 Heads and tails
fling learn beard floor

251 Witchy shadow
e. is the shadow

252 Skateboard sums
$11 - 9 = 2$ $10 - 6 = 4$
$20 - 17 = 3$ $15 - 4 = 11$

253 What is it?
teddy bear

255 Word trail
1. penguin 2. nurse 3. eggcup 4. parrot
5. toes 6. stool 7. lamp

257 Letter codes
balloon

258 Dividing
$28 \div 7 = 4$ $30 \div 6 = 5$
$18 \div 9 = 2$ $99 \div 9 = 11$

259 Hidden words
music maths

261 Word scrambles
penguin walrus castle windmill
socks gloves sweets chocolate

262 Jungly wordsearch

264 At the station
1. man's hair
2. strap on man's bag
3. stickers on suitcase
4. dog's tail
5. dog's collar
6. pattern on girl's t-shirt
7. rubbish bin missing
8. bricks on wall
9. driver's moustache
10. driver's tie missing

265 A lot of legs crossword
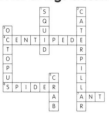

269 Missing middles
castle monkey jockey donkey

270 Clothes code
15 + 19 = 34   20 - 17 = 3   18 - 16 = 2
19 - 17 = 2   16 + 15 = 31

272 Adding-up bananas
6 + 6 + 4 + 6 + 4 = 26

273 Sums puzzles

6	−	1	=	5
+		×		+
2	×	1	=	2
=		=		=
8	−	1	=	7

5	−	3	=	2
+		÷		+
2	×	3	=	6
=		=		=
7	+	1	=	8

274 Picture wheel
lizard

275 Rhyming words
fish - dish boat - goat fox - socks train - rain

278 Creepy caterpillars
4 x 4 = 16   3 x 5 = 15   8 x 5 = 40
11 x 3 = 33   2 x 3 = 6

279 Heads and tails
broken should detail pounce

280 Puppy shadow
d. is the shadow

281 Toadstool sums
18 - 9 = 9   13 - 3 = 10
17 - 12 = 5   9 - 7= 2

282 What is it?
crocodile

284 Word trail
1. gloves 2. starfish 3. hand 4. desk 5. key
6. yacht 7. tulip 8. pig

286 Letter codes
pineapple

287 Hidden words
ate cakes

288 Dividing
48 ÷ 12 = 4   5 ÷ 5 = 1
30 ÷ 10 = 3   63 ÷ 9 = 7

289 Time for take-off
1. aeroplane is missing window
2. cloud missing
3. woman's hat
4. window on building missing
5. pilot's moustache missing
6. passenger's smile
7. stickers on suitcase
8. woman's bag buckle

291 Space wordsearch

292 Word scrambles
owl   bat   boat   anchor
camel pyramid   rocket planet

294 Party code
6 ÷ 3 = 2   5 ÷ 1 = 5   2 x 4 = 8
1 x 3 = 3   5 x 2 = 10

295 Missing letters
island gloves cloud dragon

299 Buildings crossword

302 Rhyming words

mouse - house   toy - boy
bat - rat   snake - rake

303 Picture wheel

robot

304 Sums puzzles

305 Adding-up holes

5 + 6 + 3 + 4 + 3 = 21

307 Crocodile sums

14 - 7 = 7   8 - 2 = 6
10 - 10 = 0   20 - 19 = 1

308 Ape shape

c. is the shadow

309 Heads and tails

stream frozen placed jumper

310 Multiplying ladders

6 x 2 = 12   4 x 4 = 16
3 x 9 = 27   10 x 3 = 30

311 Letter codes

snowman

313 Word trail

1. scarecrow 2. wizard 3. dress 4. snake
5. eagle 6. eggs

315 What is it?

strawberry

316 Hidden words

goals match

317 Dividing

7 ÷ 7 = 1   16 ÷ 4 = 4
27 ÷ 9 = 3   16 ÷ 2 = 8

319 Word scrambles

swan   duck   clock   watch
octopus lobster   balloon present

320 Festive fun wordsearch

322 Splish, splash

1. boy's armband
2. stripe on boy's shorts
3. girl's hair
4. spots on girl's rubber ring
5. boy's smile
6. foot in water
7. pattern on ball

323 Christmas code

10 x 6 = 60   5 x 8 = 40   9 x 7 = 63
5 x 10 = 50   9 x 8 = 72

324 Missing letters

knee queen guitar orange

328 Ready, steady, go crossword

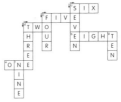

331 Sounds the same

feet bee sweets leaf tree seat beaver seal

332 Picture wheel

tricycle

333 Sums puzzle

6	+	2	=	8
÷		+		+
2	−	1	=	1
=		=		=
3	x	3	=	9

334 Adding-up balls
$4 + 3 + 3 + 2 + 4 = 16$

336 Beehive sums
$6 - 4 = 2$ $17 - 9 = 8$
$9 - 6 = 3$ $19 - 5 = 14$

337 Fairy shadows
e. is the shadow

338 Heads and tails
cracker crowded swimmer stirrup

339 Beetle sums
$1 \times 10 = 10$ $4 \times 12 = 48$ $5 \times 3 = 15$
$7 \times 6 = 42$ $7 \times 7 = 49$

340 Dividing
$48 \div 8 = 6$ $20 \div 4 = 5$
$144 \div 12 = 12$ $20 \div 2 = 10$

341 Hidden words
water snorkel

342 What is it?
helicopter

344 Word scrambles
doctor nurse fairy   witch
moon stars elephant giraffe

345 Spooky wordsearch

347 Playtime
1. hair of girl on slide
2. eyes of girl on slide
3. shoe of girl on slide
4. button missing from boy on swing
5. t-shirt of boy on swing
6. shoe of boy on swing
7. knee patch of boy under slide
8. stripes on ball

348 Happy holiday crossword

352 Plural endings
mushrooms witches fairies pumpkins

353 Halloween code
$18 + 20 = 38$ $16 + 19 = 35$ $15 + 17 = 32$
$20 - 19 = 1$ $16 - 15 = 1$

355 Adding-up eggs
$8 + 7 + 2 + 8 + 5 = 30$

356 Sums puzzle

4	+	12	=	16
+		+		-
14	-	2	=	12
=		=		=
18	-	14	=	4

357 Picture wheel
rabbit

360 Sounds the same
cloud flower cow trowel roundabout
tower loud flour

361 Give the dog a bone sums
$16 - 6 = 10$ $12 - 7 = 5$
$7 - 3 = 4$ $20 - 13 = 7$

362 Wiggly-worm sums
$4 \times 4 = 16$ $5 \times 5 = 25$ $10 \times 10 = 100$
$9 \times 9 = 81$ $2 \times 2 = 4$

363 Hidden words
time watch

364 Dividing
$8 \div 4 = 2$ $28 \div 7 = 4$
$36 \div 4 = 9$ $32 \div 2 = 16$